American Red Cross

lifeguard training

The following organizations provided expert review of the materials
and support for **American Red Cross Lifeguard Training:**

American Camping Association

BOY SCOUTS OF AMERICA

Girl Scouts.

jcc association

MWR

This participant's manual was developed and produced through the combined
efforts of the American Red Cross, external reviewers and Staywell. Without the
commitment to excellence of both paid and volunteer staff, this manual could
not have been created.

StayWell

Printed in the United States of America.

Cover and Interior Design by Studio Montage
Composition by ColorTek
Printing/Binding by Banta

Staywell
263 Summer Street
Boston, MA 02210

Library of Congress Cataloging-in-Publication Data

Lifeguard Training / American Red Cross.
   p.   cm.
   Includes bibliographical reference and index.
   ISBN 1-58480-075-5
   1. Life-saving   2. Lifeguards—Training of.   I. American Red Cross
   GV838.7.L54
   797.2'00289—dc20

                  94-19885
                  CIP

01 02 03 04 05 / 9 8 7 6 5 4 3 2 1

preface

Fifty-four percent of the population across the nation enjoys swimming as a leisure activity, and total participation exceeds all other popular activities such as walking for pleasure, cycling, golf, tennis, and boating. Since swimming is one of the top participation sports across the country and because there is an ever-increasing number of aquatic facilities being built to meet the demand, lifeguarding responsibilities have significantly changed. For people ages 1 through 24, drowning is second only to motor vehicles accidents as the cause of unintentional-injury death in the United States.

In spite of the efforts made by the many American Red Cross instructors, lifeguards, volunteers, and sponsors of water safety programs, drownings and near-drownings do occur. Aquatic injuries can happen at any time or place for a number of reasons. Because situations like these occur, it is essential that lifeguards receive proper training.

Lifeguards must be able to recognize hazardous situations to prevent injury. They must be able to supervise swimmers, minimize dangers, educate facility users about safety, enforce rules and regulations, give assistance, and prepare records and reports. The position of the lifeguard today has become one of greater responsibility than in the past.

In the new millennium, lifeguards face a host of new challenges: infectious diseases, medical waste, increased skin cancer risk, crowd control, violence, new technologies, and environmental issues. More and more facilities have been adding waterpark attractions, which greatly increase attendance and the need for vigilance. Medical research has demonstrated the effectiveness of interventions through defibrillation and oxygen. Increased levels of education, training, and preventive measures are all used by today's professionals to meet these challenges. This evolution is indicative of the increasingly important role lifeguards play in their communities. Rather than remaining static, lifeguards have expanded their horizons to successfully meet these challenges.

brief
table of contents

table
of contents

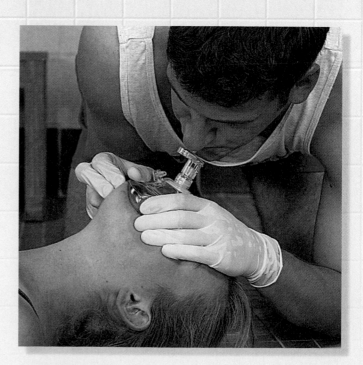

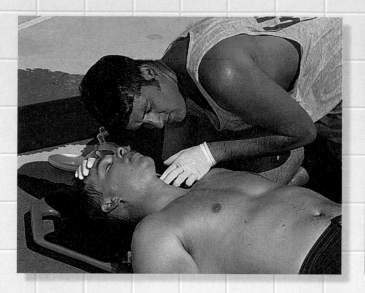

chapter 1

professional
lifeguard

Fig. 1-1

Today you begin training for an exciting and rewarding job. Being a lifeguard is—

- *Dynamic—Each day on the job may present new situations.*
- *Challenging—Doing your job well requires quick judgments.*
- *Exciting—You may respond at any moment to an emergency.*
- *Important—Your knowledge, skills, and attitude can save a life.*

This chapter describes the characteristics and responsibilities of a lifeguard, the rewards of being a professional lifeguard, and the importance of keeping your knowledge and skills sharp.

Characteristics of a Professional Lifeguard

Lifeguard professionalism begins with training and certification. Professional lifeguards are mentally, physically, and emotionally prepared at all times to do their job (Fig. 1-1). As a professional lifeguard, you must be—

Reliable—Get to work on time, accept assignments willingly, be committed to your work, and respond to all incidents quickly and effectively.

Mature—As a lifeguard, you are a leader. Act responsibly, obey all facility rules, and lead others by your example.

Courteous and Consistent—Be polite and enforce the rules firmly and equally for everyone.

Positive—Show your positive attitude in all your actions.

Professional—Look and be prepared to respond appropriately in any situation:

- Wear your uniform only when on duty.
- Be well groomed.
- Keep your rescue equipment with you at all times and positioned for an immediate response.
- Keep essential personal gear, such as sunglasses, on or near you at all times.
- Sit or stand erect at your lifeguarding station.
- Keep your eyes on your area of responsibility at all times.
- Keep interactions with others short and do not let them interrupt your primary responsibilities.
- Transfer and handle equipment carefully.
- Observe all facility rules, regulations, and policies.
- Eat only when on break or off duty.

Healthy and fit—In an emergency, you will need to respond with a burst of strenuous activity. Being healthy and physically fit helps you stay alert and gives you strength and energy to prevent and respond to emergencies. You can stay healthy and fit by—

Exercising. Regular exercise helps you—

- Respond quickly in any situation.
- Perform strenuous rescues.
- Stay alert.
- Cope with stress and fatigue.
- Stay healthy.

Eating Properly. Good nutrition and a balanced diet give you the energy you need to stay alert and active. Drink plenty of water to prevent dehydration.

Using Sun Protection. Overexposure to the sun can cause many problems:

- Sunburn
- Skin cancer
- Heat exhaustion
- Heat stroke

Help prevent these problems by using a sunscreen with a sun protection factor (SPF) of at least 15 and by wearing clothing, like a shirt and a hat that covers your head and provides shade for your face and ears. You can also use an umbrella for shade. Remember to wear sunglasses with UVA/UVB protection to protect your eyes and reduce glare.

Not Using Alcohol and Other Drugs. Never use alcohol and other drugs on the job. It is a serious offense. On- or off-duty use of alcohol and other drugs can negatively affect your job performance and can jeopardize the safety of patrons and co-workers.

Benefits of Being a Professional Lifeguard

Effective lifeguarding requires commitment and a lot of effort, but the benefits you receive are well worth the effort. You will—

- Know your actions can save a life.
- Be proud to accept challenges and meet the facility's standards.
- Develop leadership, public relations, conflict resolution, and teamwork skills.
- Gain discipline and decision-making skills that help prepare you for your future.

Responsibilities of a Professional Lifeguard

Your primary responsibility as a lifeguard is to ensure patron safety and protect lives—including your own. You can do this in several ways:

- Prevent injuries by minimizing or eliminating hazardous situations or behaviors.
- Enforce facility rules and regulations and educate patrons about them.
- Recognize and respond effectively to all emergencies.
- Administer first aid or CPR in an emergency, and if trained, give oxygen and use an automated external defibrillator if needed.
- Inform other lifeguards and facility staff when you need more help or equipment.

Other tasks you do as a lifeguard are called secondary responsibilities. Secondary responsibilities must never prevent you from meeting your primary responsibilities. For example, you may—

- Help patrons find a missing person.
- Fill out required records and reports on schedule and submit them to the proper person or office.
- Do maintenance or other tasks assigned by your supervisor. (Some duties, such as monitoring pool chemistry, require training beyond this lifeguard training course.)

Lifeguarding TIP: Never perform secondary responsibilities when you are doing patron surveillance.

job description
for a Lifeguard

Job Title: Lifeguard (entry-level)

Job Description:

Responsible for ensuring the safety of facility patrons by preventing and responding to emergencies

Minimum Qualifications:

Current certification in the following:

- American Red Cross Lifeguard Training/First Aid
- American Red Cross CPR for the Professional Rescuer

and

- American Red Cross Waterfront Lifeguarding for non-surf open water positions
- American Red Cross Waterpark Lifeguarding for waterpark and multi-attraction facility positions
- Other certifications required by local or state laws
- Pre-employment testing of lifeguarding skills and knowledge

Knowledge and Skills:

- Thorough knowledge and application of lifeguarding surveillance and rescue techniques
- An understanding of facility characteristics, rules, policies, and procedures
- Leadership and public relations skills
- Decision-making skills

Responsibilities:

- Recognize and respond effectively in emergencies.
- Enforce all aquatic facility policies, rules, and regulations.
- Inspect the facility on a daily schedule and report any unsafe conditions or equipment to the supervisor.
- Complete records and reports.
- Participate in regular in-service training sessions.
- Exercise regularly to maintain fitness level (strength and endurance).
- Complete additional duties as assigned by supervisor.

Responsible To:

Head lifeguard, pool manager, or aquatics director/supervisor

Decision-Making

Decision-making is important in lifeguarding as it is in other areas in life. As a lifeguard you will make many kinds of decisions, including—

- When and how to make a rescue.
- When and how to perform first aid and give other emergency care.
- How to work with your lifeguard team and the facility's management.
- How to interact with patrons and deal with both emergency and non-emergency problems.

Decision-making can be difficult, especially in an emergency. Sometimes a person makes a decision quickly without thinking about all the possible consequences. To make informed decisions, use a decision-making model.

FIND MODEL ACTIVITY

Directions: Read the following scenario and answer the following question using the FIND model.

The Facts: A patron who comes to your station is upset. He believes teenagers stole some items from his locker. He points at two teenagers coming out of the locker room and accuses them, even though he did not actually see them steal. How do you handle this situation using the FIND model?

Figure out the problem and write it below.

_____

Identify possible solutions for the problem and write them below.

1.
2.
3.

Name pros and cons for each possible solution and write them below.

Pros:

Cons:

Pros:

Cons:

Pros:

Cons:

Decide which solution is best and write it below.

_____
_____
_____
_____

This will help you clearly understand what is involved in the decision. The FIND model is an effective decision-making model. FIND means—

- F = Figure out the problem.
- I = Identify possible solutions.
- N = Name pros and cons for each solution.
- D = Decide which solution is best.

The FIND approach applied to lifeguarding decisions will help you FIND the best action to take in most situations.

Lifeguarding TIP: Making a good decision in a non-emergency situation can help prevent emergencies.

Legal Considerations

As a professional lifeguard, you should understand the following legal terms:

- **Duty to act**—While on the job as a lifeguard, you have a legal responsibility to act in an emergency.
- **Standard of care**—You are expected to meet a minimum standard of care, which may be established in part by your training program and in part by state or local authorities. This standard requires you to—
  - Provide proper information and warnings to help prevent injuries.
  - Recognize a person in an emergency.
  - Rescue a person needing assistance.
  - Give first aid and emergency care according to your level of training.
- **Negligence**—If you fail to follow the standard of care and that results in someone being injured or more seriously injured, you may be considered negligent. Negligence includes—
  - Failing to provide care.
  - Giving care beyond your training.
  - Providing inappropriate care.
  - Failing to control or stop behavior that could result in injury.
- **Good Samaritan Laws**—Most states have Good Samaritan Laws that protect people who give emergency care. These laws, which differ from state to state, may protect you from legal liability as long as you act in good faith, are not negligent, and act as you have been trained to act. Check your local and state laws to see if Good Samaritan laws protect you.
- **Consent**—You must have permission from an injured person before you give first aid and emergency care. If the person cannot give consent for some reason but obviously needs emergency care, the law assumes this victim would give consent if able to do so. The same is true for minors when a parent or guardian is not present.
- **Refusal of Care**—Some ill or injured people, even those who desperately need care, may refuse care. Even though the victim may be seriously injured, you must honor his or her wishes. However, you should explain to the person why he or she needs care. **Always document any refusal of care.**
- **Abandonment**—Once you begin giving care, you must continue your care until Emergency Medical Services (EMS) personnel or someone with equal or greater training arrives and takes over. You can be held legally responsible for abandoning a person in need if you leave the scene or stop giving care.

LEGAL CONSIDERATIONS ACTIVITY

Directions: Read the following scenario and answer the questions.
FACTS: An 8-year-old girl enters the water from a diving board and swims to the bottom of the pool. She does not surface. There are four lifeguards on duty. A patron in the pool also happens to be certified as a lifeguard but does not work at this facility.

Question: Do the lifeguards have a duty to act? Why or why not?

_____

_____

_____

Question: What should the lifeguards do following this incident?

_____

_____

_____

- **Confidentiality**—While making a rescue or giving care, you may learn something about an ill or injured person that is private and confidential. Do not share this information with anyone except law enforcement or EMS personnel.
- **Record Keeping**—Documenting injuries and incidents is very important. If a legal action occurs later on, a record can also provide legal documentation of what you saw, heard, and did at the scene. Be familiar with the forms at your facility and know how to complete them.

The Lifeguard Team

Whenever another lifeguard is on duty with you, you are part of a lifeguard team. Your team may be trained and evaluated together. Team members practice working together as a unit. Everyone who works at the facility needs to know what to do in an emergency and how and when to call for more help. To be a good team, all staff must practice the facility's emergency action plans (EAPs) together until everyone knows their parts well and can perform them correctly. EAPs are the written procedures that tell lifeguards and other staff what to do in emergencies.

Team members work together better when they know what management expects from them and what they can expect from each other. Management should put its expectations in an employee handbook or other written guidelines. To learn what you and other team members can expect from each other, you need to talk and practice together. On-the-job or in-service training is ideal for reviewing and practicing EAPs and talking with your teammates.

How Facility Management Promotes Lifeguard Professionalism

Management should help you become a professional lifeguard. Management should support you by giving you—

- A policies and procedures manual.
- Orientation, in-service, and annual training.
- Opportunities for recognition and career development.

If your facility does not have professional development opportunities like those described below, talk to your supervisor. He or she may be able to develop these opportunities for you or help you find other options.

Policies and Procedures Manual

Management should make sure that you have the information you need to work safely and to perform your duties effectively. A policies and procedures manual can provide this information. This manual usually includes—

- Administrative policies and procedures.
- Rules and regulations.
- Emergency action plans.
- Sample record and report forms.
- Guidelines for pool activities (swim lessons, fitness classes, and diving).
- Guidelines for personnel (including hiring policies, conditions of employment, and standards of performance and conduct).
- An organizational chart (with a chain of command and job descriptions).
- A floor plan of the facility that shows emergency evacuation routes.
- Instructions for equipment use.
- Diagrams of areas of responsibility for patron surveillance.

Orientation

An orientation session about facility operations and lifeguards' responsibilities helps both new and returning lifeguards understand the facility, their responsibilities, and management's expectations. Ask questions of your employer and become familiar with your facility's operations.

In-service Training

In-service training helps you keep your knowledge and skills sharp. The facility manager, a head lifeguard, or someone in the community, such as a public health official, may conduct sessions (Fig. 1-2). In-service training sessions may address issues like these:

Fig. 1-2

- Potential hazards at the facility.
- Facility rules and regulations.
- Emergency action plans.
- Surveillance and water rescue skills.
- First aid, CPR, and head, neck, or back injury and, when appropriate, bloodborne pathogens, oxygen administration, and automated external defibrillator (AED) skills training.
- Physical conditioning.
- Decision-making.
- Internal staff issues such as communication, teamwork, and morale.

Lifeguarding TIP: As a professional lifeguard, you need to regularly participate in in-service training sessions.

Annual Training

You should have annual training, especially if you work as a seasonal lifeguard. Annual training may include CPR review courses, lifeguard training review courses, and review of lifeguarding knowledge and skills. Talk to your facility manager about annual training opportunities.

Recognition and Career Development

You may be recognized for a job well done by an award, a promotion, or simply a pat on the back. Some facilities offer career opportunities through in-service training, special events like lifeguard competitions, additional training or course work, or attending conferences or workshops. The American Red Cross offers basic- and instructor-level courses and modules to enhance your career, such as water-park lifeguarding, waterfront lifeguarding, oxygen administration, bloodborne pathogens, automated external defibrillation, and lifeguard management.

Maintaining Your Skills and Knowledge

Receiving your American Red Cross Lifeguard Training certificate means that you have successfully completed the course material and passed the written and skill tests. It does not mean that you have learned everything there is to know about lifeguarding. You need to keep working on being professional by keeping your skills and knowledge sharp. This is especially important for seasonal lifeguards, who can lose knowledge and skills during the off season. Attend workshops, join an aquatic association, read aquatic literature and periodicals, and talk with other lifeguards about their ideas. One of the best ways to stay current in your skills and knowledge and stay in peak physical form is to participate in in-service training sessions.

Putting it All Together

Being a professional lifeguard means being fully prepared for this challenging and important work. Looking and acting professional shows others that you are prepared to do the job. Staying professional requires practice and commitment.

Preparing for lifeguarding responsibilities is what this course is all about. Throughout your training, remember that no one is a natural born lifeguard; it takes hard work. But with practice and dedication, you can meet the challenges and gain the rewards of being a professional lifeguard.

in review...

Circle the letter of the best answer or answers.

1. **A lifeguard's primary responsibilities include—**
   a. Preventing injuries by minimizing or eliminating hazardous situations or behaviors.
   b. Administering first aid or CPR in an emergency.
   c. Recognizing and responding quickly and effectively in all emergencies.
   d. Helping patrons locate a missing person.
   e. Enforcing facility rules and regulations and educating patrons about them.
   f. Informing other lifeguards and facility staff when more help and/or equipment is needed.

2. **A lifeguard's secondary responsibilities include—**
   a. Filling out all required records and reports on schedule and submitting them to the proper person or office.
   b. Educating patrons about rules and regulations.
   c. Conducting surveillance.
   d. Doing maintenance or other tasks assigned by the supervisor.

3. **The important characteristics of a professional lifeguard include—**
   a. Reliability.
   b. Maturity.
   c. A sense of humor.
   d. Courtesy and consistency.
   e. Positive attitude.

4. **If a lifeguard fails to give care, tries to give care he or she is not trained to do, or gives incorrect care, he or she may be—**
   a. Breaking confidentiality.
   b. Breaking Good Samaritan laws.
   c. Abandoning the patron.
   d. Being negligent.
   e. Failing to obtain consent.

Circle True or False:

5. Once you have received your American Red Cross Lifeguard Training certificate, you will keep your knowledge and skills for the duration of your certification and will be aware of everything there is to know about lifeguarding.

   True   False

Fill in the blanks.

6. Where would you expect to find the facility's written emergency action plan? _____

   _____

7. In-service training is— _____

   _____

   _____

8. Identify three or more ways to stay professional by maintaining your skills and knowledge:

   _____

   _____

   _____

   _____

chapter 2

injury
prevention
and facility safety

The lifeguard is essential for keeping an aquatic facility safe. Unlike other professional rescuers, lifeguards are present before potential injuries happen and can act to prevent them. You will focus most of your time on injury prevention, which means preventing situations in which patrons can be harmed. Therefore, you need to understand how injuries occur and how you can help prevent them.

Preventing Injuries: Patron Safety

Aquatic injury prevention is a part of the facility's risk management program. Risk management involves identifying dangerous conditions or behaviors that can cause injuries and then taking steps to minimize or eliminate them. As a lifeguard, you will perform emergency rescues, but you will spend far more time in preventive lifeguarding trying to make sure emergencies do not happen in the first place.

Although you cannot prevent all injuries, knowing what causes life-threatening injuries helps you prevent them. An injury results from physical harm to the body. Injuries are either life threatening or nonlife threatening. Examples of life-threatening injuries include—

- Submersion (near-drowning or drowning).
- Injuries to the head, neck, or back (spinal injuries).
- Injuries that cause unconsciousness and difficulty breathing.
- Severe bleeding.

The two most serious aquatic emergencies to prevent are drowning and head, neck, or back injuries. Drowning happens when a person suffocates in the water. Most head, neck, or back injuries result from head-first entries into shallow water. If a victim's head hits the bottom or the side of the pool, the spinal cord can be injured. This can cause possible paralysis or death.

Nonlife-threatening injuries also occur in aquatic facilities. Examples of nonlife-threatening injuries include—

- Suspected fracture or dislocation.
- Abrasions (scrapes).
- Superficial burns (sunburns).
- Muscle cramps (caused by overexertion).

Understanding how injuries occur helps you know how to prevent them by—

- Increasing your awareness of risks and hazards.
- Helping patrons avoid risky behavior.
- Developing a safety-conscious attitude at your facility.

Lifeguards use three injury-prevention strategies:

1. Communication with patrons
2. Facility safety checks
3. Patron surveillance (covered in Chapter 3)

Communication with Patrons

Communication as an injury-prevention strategy requires lifeguards to—

- Inform patrons about the potential for injury.
- Educate patrons about inappropriate behavior.
- Enforce rules and regulations that prevent injury.

Inform Patrons About the Potential for Injury

Patrons need to know about risks that could cause injury. Signs give them warnings, tell them how to use equipment, and list rules and regulations to help prevent behaviors that can lead to injury. Lifeguards also help inform patrons about the potential for injuries. Therefore, lifeguards need to understand the rules and regulations of the facility where they work.

Rules and Regulations

Every facility should have rules and regulations posted (Fig. 2-1). Your job is to understand these rules and help patrons understand and comply with them. Use a positive approach to promote acceptable behavior. For example, if a patron is running on the deck, explain the acceptable behavior: "Please walk."

Rules do not keep patrons from having fun. They are for everyone's health and safety, including facility staff. Posted rules help patrons enjoy their experience without endangering themselves or others. Rules should be posted in plain view for all patrons and staff to see. Rules posted at aquatic facilities should include—

- Swim only when a lifeguard is on duty.
- Obey lifeguard instructions at all times.
- No running, pushing, or horseplay.
- Only one person at a time on the diving board.
- Check the water area in front of the diving board before diving.
- Dive only in designated areas.
- Shower with soap before entering the water.
- No glass containers in the pool area.
- No alcohol or other drug use.

The facility may also have other rules, such as—

- Only members and their guests allowed.
- Nonswimmers and children under a set age or height must be supervised by an adult.
- Children using flotation devices must be supervised by a parent or guardian and within arm's reach. No personal flotation devices (PFDs) allowed except for U.S. Coast Guard–approved life jackets.
- Patrons may have to demonstrate their swimming ability before entering deep water.

Facility Equipment and Structures

There are other rules for specific equipment and structures. These rules depend on the facility.

- One person at a time on a ladder.
- Do not sit or hang on lifelines.
- Do not climb on lifeguard stands or towers.
- Lap swimmers may use kick-boards, hand paddles, pull buoys, masks, fins, and snorkels only for swimming in assigned lanes.
- Starting blocks may be used only in scheduled practices, competitions, and instruction when supervised by a coach or instructor (Fig. 2-2).

Diving Areas

Rules for diving boards and towers should be posted in the diving area (Fig. 2-3).

- Only one person on the diving board at a time.
- Use the ladder to climb to the diving board.
- Look before diving or jumping to make sure no one is in the diving area.
- Only one bounce allowed on the diving board.
- Dive or jump straight out from the diving board.
- Swim immediately to the closest ladder or wall.
- Dive only when supervised by a lifeguard, swimming instructor, or coach.

Fig. 2-1

Fig. 2-2

Fig. 2-3

Spas, Hot Tubs, and Therapy Pools

Spas, hot tubs, and therapy pools are popular. Their hazards include drowning, hyperthermia (high body temperature), and disease transmission. State and local laws may regulate their operation. Ask your supervisor about regulations governing spas, hot tubs, and therapy pools at your facility. Rules common to these pools include—

- Use only with a lifeguard present.
- Shower with soap before using.
- Enter and exit slowly and cautiously.
- People with heart disease, diabetes, high or low blood pressure, seizures, epilepsy, or other medical conditions are not allowed to use the spa.
- Pregnant women should seek their doctor's approval before using a spa or hot tub.
- No unsupervised use by children.
- No children under 5 years of age allowed in the spa. (Children cannot cope physically with the heat, which may cause hyperthermia and other harmful effects.)

- Do not use the spa while under the influence of alcohol or other drugs.
- No diving, jumping, or horseplay in the spa.
- Limit time in spa to 10 minutes. Patrons may then shower, cool down, and return again briefly. Prolonged use may result in nausea, dizziness, fainting, or hyperthermia.
- No body lotions, oils, or sunscreen in spa.
- No food or drink in spa area.
- No exercising in the spa.
- Report any safety issues to the lifeguard.

Play Structures

Play structures are common at many facilities and come in many shapes and sizes. Permanent play structures include tube and drop slides, rope swings, sprays, fountains, and moving water (Fig. 2-4). Removable play structures include floating toys, large inflatables, and water games. Play structures guidelines include—

- Follow manufacturer's guidelines.
- Do not let a play structure become overcrowded.
- Only clean and soft toys allowed in the water.
- No climbing on inflatable play structures on dry land.

If the facility has play structures, extra precautions are needed. Careful observation helps patrons stay safe and keeps the play structure in good condition. Be alert for—

- The excitement of using play structures makes some nonswimmers or weak swimmers careless. They might try things they would not otherwise do, or they might unexpectedly enter deep water.
- Swimmers can be surprised by the fall from a drop slide or rope swing, especially if they did not realize they are over deep water. Watch that they come up to the surface and swim to the side.
- Excited children may run, fall, and be injured around sprays and fountains in shallow water. A very young child who falls may not be able to get back up.

Fig. 2-4

- Moving water can cause patrons to lose their balance and fall over.
- Patrons may jump into the water from floating toys and inflatables, without noticing what is around them, and land on other swimmers.

Some play structures require their own lifeguards; others are watched by lifeguards surveying a larger area. Watching these structures depends on—

- Location of the feature.
- Number of patrons in the facility.
- Number of patrons using the structures.
- Age and skill of patrons using the structures.
- Activity and excitement level.
- Lifeguard's ability to see around and under tethered structures.

Guidelines for permanent slides include—

- Follow manufacturer's guidelines for all slides.
- Enforce age, height, and weight guidelines.
- Only one rider allowed on the slide at a time.
- Enter, ride, and exit the slide feet-first.
- Keep hands inside the slide.
- No standing, stopping, or sliding down headfirst.
- Keep slide entry and exit points clear.
- No metal objects, locker keys, jewelry, metal snaps/zippers, eyewear, or watches.
- Station lifeguards at the top and bottom of slides.

Educate Patrons About Inappropriate Behavior

Patrons may be unfamiliar with a facility's features or get so excited that they do not read signs or pay attention to the rules. You may have to let them know what could happen because of an unsafe act. Explaining rules in a positive way encourages patrons to behave safely. Use these four steps to prevent a patron from engaging in risky behavior:

1. *Get the person's attention.* You may blow your whistle and say, "Excuse me, but what you are doing is dangerous."

2. *Explain the hazard or danger.* Simply telling them not to do something often does not work. People usually understand and cooperate better when they know why something is dangerous. You can say, "The water in this area is too shallow for diving."

3. *Explain how they might be injured.* You can say, "Diving into shallow water can cause you to hit your head on the bottom and be injured."

EDUCATING PATRONS ABOUT INAPPROPRIATE BEHAVIOR ACTIVITY

Directions: Read the following scenarios and answer the questions. Use the four steps to prevent a patron from engaging in risky behavior.

The Facts: A teenage boy dove into an area of the pool designated as "No Diving."

How would you communicate the "No Diving" rule to him using the four steps for educating patrons?

The Facts: The teenage patron becomes angry and refuses to obey the rule. How would you handle this situation using the FIND model?

Figure out the problem and write it below.

_____

_____

Identify possible solutions for the problem and write them below.

1.

2.

3.

Name pros and cons for each possible solution and write them below.

Pros:

Cons:

Pros:

Cons:

Pros:

Cons:

Decide which solution is best and write it below.

_____

_____

_____

---

4. *Explain what to do to avoid being injured.* You can say, "If you want to dive, do it in the deep end of the pool, where it is safe." Or you could say, "Excuse me, diving into shallow water is dangerous and can cause head injury. Please use the deep end."

This type of explanation—

- Gets the patron's attention.
- Tells him or her what the danger is.
- Emphasizes the consequences of the risky behavior.
- Offers safe alternatives for what the patron wants to do.

Dealing with Uncooperative Patrons and Violence

No matter how fairly you enforce rules, you may encounter an uncooperative patron. But before you assume a patron is uncooperative, make sure that he or she hears and understands you.

Uncooperative behavior may occur for different reasons:

- Some patrons let their fun get out of hand.
- Some patrons do not understand you because of language barriers.
- Some patrons may be under the influence of alcohol and other drugs.
- Conflicts between some patrons keep them from paying attention to the rules.

If a patron breaks rules and is uncooperative, take action right away because breaking rules is a danger to the uncooperative patron and others. Most facilities have procedures for handling uncooperative patrons. If yours does not, call the head lifeguard or facility manager for help as soon as possible.

A patron may threaten or commit a violent act with a weapon like a knife or a gun, an object like a bottle or a stick, or a fist or foot. Be realistic about what you can do in a violent situation. If you think that violence is about to erupt, notify the head lifeguard or facility manager immediately. If violence does erupt, do not try to stop it. Do not confront a violent person physically or verbally. NEVER approach a patron who has a weapon. Retreat and follow your facility's emergency action plan for violence. Remember that safety is still your main goal: safety for patrons and yourself.

Enforce Rules and Regulations That Prevent Injury

Enforcing rules helps prevent injuries and leads to patrons having safer attitudes. When enforcing rules, always be consistent and fair. Maybe the patron is confused or just does not understand the rule. Different enforcement methods work better for patrons at different ages. Use methods as directed by facility policies.

You can deal with children who keep breaking rules by having them sit out of the water for a set time. You can also ask an off-duty lifeguard to read and explain the rules to them. If their parent or guardian seems uncooperative, make your point clearly but do not get into an argument.

RULE ENFORCEMENT ACTIVITY

Directions: Check all characteristics of effective rule enforcement:

- ☐ Be fair with all patrons.
- ☐ Yell loudly to make your point.
- ☐ Remove a whole group from the water if one person breaks a rule.
- ☐ Let patrons break minor rules if you think no one will be hurt.
- ☐ Adjust the rules you enforce depending on the patron's age.
- ☐ When necessary, tell patrons the reason for a rule.
- ☐ Using a positive approach is more effective than being harsh.
- ☐ Enforce height and weight requirements for certain areas.
- ☐ Never tell a patron how they could be injured if they break a rule.

If necessary, ask the head lifeguard or facility manager for help.

Since most people want to be treated with respect, just explaining the rules is usually enough. If someone keeps breaking the rules, however, you may have to tell the person to leave the facility for the safety of all patrons. Do this only as a last resort. If a patron keeps breaking the rules, the head lifeguard or facility manager may even have to call the police or security personnel. The pool may be temporarily cleared until the situation is over. Every facility needs a procedure for removing someone from the facility. This procedure should have specific steps and guidelines to follow. Record any such action in the facility's daily log or report.

Safety Checks

Safety checks are your primary method of facility surveillance. These checks are done when opening the facility, during daily operations, and at closing. Several facility safety checks are done each day. If you find an unsafe condition, correct it if possible before the facility opens. If you cannot correct the problem, tell the head lifeguard or facility manager immediately. If the condition is serious, the head lifeguard or facility manager may close or delay the opening of the pool until the condition is corrected. You can also use signs, ropes, or cones to keep patrons from the area when the facility is not open to the public

(Fig 2-5). Tell other lifeguards about the hazard so that they can direct patrons away from the area. Record all such incidents in the daily log.

Fig. 2-5

Lifeguarding Tip: Never do safety checks while performing patron surveillance.

Specific Areas to Inspect for Safety

When you do a safety check, use the facility's safety checklist form. The five general areas to inspect for safety are the—

- Deck.
- Pool.
- Locker rooms.
- Recreational equipment and play structures.
- Chemical storage areas.

SAMPLE FACILITY SAFETY CHECKLIST

	Yes	No	Action Taken	Date of Safety Check	Action Needed
Deck					
Safety equipment in good condition					
Rescue tubes and straps in good condition					
Backboards with head immobilizers and straps readily accessible					
First aid station clean					
First aid equipment- AED and oxygen equipment accessible; supplies accessible and well stocked					
Telephones working properly					
Deck not slippery and in good condition					
Deck clear of patrons' belongings					
All equipment used by patrons stored properly					
Lifeguard stands clean and in good condition					
Deck clear of standing water					
Deck clear of glass objects					
Pool					
Ladders secured properly					
Ladder handles clean and rust free					
Steps not slippery and in good condition					
Ramp not slippery and in good condition					

SAMPLE FACILITY SAFETY CHECKLIST—cont'd

	Yes	No	Action Taken	Date of Safety Check	Action Needed
Pool—cont'd					
Drain covers secured properly					
Drain covers clean					
Lifelines and buoys in order					
Water clarity satisfactory					
Water color satisfactory					
Pool free of debris					
Gutters clean					
Water temperature in pool satisfactory					
Water temperature in spa satisfactory					
Locker Rooms					
All areas clean and free of algae					
Floors clean and not slippery					
Showers in good condition (no drips)					
Liquid soap available					
Drains clean					
Wastebaskets empty					
Drinking fountains and sinks clean and in good working order					
Signs in good condition and properly displayed					
Walls clean and free of markings					
Toilets and urinals clean					
Mirrors clean and unbroken					
No unpleasant odors					
Toilet tissue available					
Paper towels available					
Doors and windows working properly (including locks)					
No broken pins on locker keys					
All articles removed from lockers daily					
Collapsible shower seats in upright position					
Locker benches clean					
Locker rooms clear of glass objects					

SAMPLE FACILITY SAFETY CHECKLIST—cont'd

	Yes	No	Action Taken	Date of Safety Check	Action Needed
Recreational Equipment and Play Structures					
Ladders to diving boards not slippery and in good condition					
Rails at diving boards clean and in good condition					
Diving boards clean and not slippery					
Diving apparatus in good condition					
Movable fulcrums locked in forward position					
Removable starting blocks stored properly					
Access to permanent starting blocks restricted					
Play structures clean, in good condition, and not slippery					
Nonmoving parts on play structures secure					
Joints on play structures move freely					
Removable play structures placed far enough from the deck and from other structures					
Removable play structures tethered properly:					
■ Attachment points secure					
■ Hooks and connections in good condition with no sharp edges					
■ Tethers not worn or frayed					
■ Seams on play structures have no gaps or leaks					
■ Water slides smooth and in good condition					
■ Inflatable play structures have the correct air pressure					
■ "Flow-through" inflatable play structures have pump attached securely, are located in a safe place, and are plugged into the appropriate electrical circuit					
Removable play structures stored properly					
Water flows properly on slides					
Landing pads under slides in good condition, securely fastened, and with no gaps to cause tripping					
Equipment such as kickboards stored properly					
Chemical Storage Areas					
Chemicals stored properly					
Doors labeled properly					
Signs legible and in good condition					
Doors locked					
No suspicious odors					
Emergency equipment is readily accessible and in good working condition					

SAFETY CHECKLIST ACTIVITY

Directions: Place a check in the appropriate column(s) in which the following items would be checked during the day.

Items to be Checked	Opening Safety Check	On-duty Safety Check	Closing Safety Check
▪ Pool, deck, and locker rooms are free of hazardous conditions	X	/	
▪ At an outdoor facility, equipment is secured to prevent theft and weather damage	X	/	
▪ All safety equipment in the facility is properly placed and in working order	X	/	
▪ Turn on the lights and test the public address system if there is one	X	/	
▪ Areas or items used by patrons	X	/	
▪ Site secured	X	/	
▪ Weather conditions	X	/	
▪ Equipment conditions	X	/	
▪ Rescue tubes in good condition and ready to use	X		
▪ Play structure conditions	X		
▪ Patrons and staff have exited the facility	X		
▪ Backboards with head immobilizers and straps are readily accessible	X		
▪ Telephones are in working order	X		
▪ Pool, deck, and locker rooms are clean	X		
▪ First aid station equipment and supplies are well stocked and ready to use	X		
▪ Daily log completed and signed	X		
▪ Water conditions	X		

Weather Conditions

Weather affects the safety of swimmers both outdoors and indoors. Know what weather conditions to look for in your area and how to act. Some state weather bureaus and local television stations have a 24-hour telephone service for weather reports. These telephone numbers should be posted with the emergency telephone numbers at your facility. Local radio stations and television channels also provide weather reports throughout the day. In remote areas, you may get additional information from a weather radio, CB radio, or scanner. Always follow your facility's emergency action plan for severe weather conditions.

Lightning and Thunderstorms

Lightning and thunderstorms happen more often in the summer. Follow your facility's policy for clearing patrons from the water before an impending storm. Do not risk patron safety. If a storm or other bad weather is predicted, stay alert for signs of the storm coming, such as thunder and lightning or high winds. According to the National Lightning Safety Institute (NLSI), wait 30 minutes after the thunder and lightning stop entirely before letting patrons get back into the water. Then keep watching for more storms and listen to weather reports on the radio.

Safety Guidelines for Lightning

▪ Clear everyone from the water at the first sound of thunder or first sight of lightning. Move patrons inside to a safe area. Large buildings are safer than smaller or open structures like picnic shelters or gazebos.

- Keep patrons and staff out of showers and locker rooms during a thunderstorm. Water and metal can conduct the lightning.
- Do not use the telephone except in emergencies.
- Keep everyone away from windows and metal objects (i.e., door frames).
- Know your facility's emergency action plan (EAP) for severe weather.

If caught outside in a thunderstorm with not enough time to reach a safe building—

- Keep everyone away from structures in open areas, such as picnic shelters.
- Keep away from tall trees standing alone and any tall structures.
- Keep away from water and metal objects, such as metal fences, tanks, rails, and pipes.
- Position yourself as low as possible: squat or crouch with your knees drawn up, both feet together, and hands off the ground. Do not lie flat on the ground; minimize ground contact.

Heavy Rain and Hail

Heavy rain and hail can be dangerous. Rain can keep you from seeing the bottom of the pool or beneath the surface of the water at waterfronts. Clear patrons from the water and direct them to shelter.

Tornadoes

Listen to weather forecasts if your area is prone to tornadoes. A tornado *watch* means that tornadoes are possible. A tornado *warning* means that a tornado has been sighted and that everyone should take shelter immediately.

Safety Guidelines for Tornadoes

- Clear the water and area.
- Move everyone to the location specified in your facility's emergency action plan (EAP), such as a basement or an inside area on the lowest level of a building.
- Keep everyone away from windows, doors, and outside walls.
- If no shelter is available, have everyone lie flat in a ditch or on a low section of ground.
- If you hear a tornado siren warning, keep patrons in the safe location until the all-clear signal is sounded.

High Wind

High wind may cause waves or turbulence that makes it hard to see patrons in the water. Wind also increases the risk of hypothermia (low body temperature), especially for small children and the elderly.

Safety Guidelines for High Wind

- Clear the pool or waterfront if you cannot see the bottom or beneath the surface.
- Move all patrons and staff indoors.
- If possible and safe to do so, secure all facility equipment that could be blown and become dangerous.

Fog

In some areas, fog can occur at any time of the day or night with changing weather conditions. If the fog limits visibility, the facility may need to be closed.

Weather Conditions and Indoor Facilities

Indoor facilities are safe from most weather problems but still may be affected. An indoor facility may or may not be grounded to protect patrons from lightning. Follow the guidelines for severe weather described in the facility's operations manual. Severe weather can also cause a power failure. The facility should have some type of portable or emergency lighting in case of a power failure. In cases of power failure or if there is no lightning protection, clear the pool and deck immediately. Patrons may wait in locker room areas until the pool reopens.

Management and Safety

Just as you have a responsibility to protect patrons, management has an obligation to protect you, as well as the patrons you are lifeguarding. The management must—

- Warn patrons and staff about actual and potential dangers.
- Address unsafe or dangerous conditions.
- Comply with local, state, and federal regulations.
- Keep records on the facility and its employees.
- Assist after an emergency.

Warn Patrons and Staff

Management can help prevent injuries by posting signs, markings, and warnings to inform patrons about dangers (Figs. 2-6 & 2-7). Management must also protect staff members from dangers at the facility by giving you specific written and spoken information, as well as protective equipment.

Address Unsafe Conditions

You work with management to address unsafe conditions at your facility (Fig. 2-8). Management tells you what to look for during your safety checks. Management relies on you to find and report dangers. When you have found and reported an unsafe condition, management is responsible for correcting it.

Fig. 2-6

Fig. 2-7

Fig. 2-8

Comply with Regulations

Government regulations protect people. The facility and staff must comply with all regulations. The following sections describe some federal regulations that affect you.

Hazard Communication Standard

Federal regulations protect people from chemical hazards in and around the facility. For example, the Hazard Communication Standard has rules about hazardous chemicals to prevent illness and injury caused by an exposure. Management has to give you information and training about the chemicals stored and used at your workplace if your job involves handling them (Fig. 2-9). Each chemical has an information sheet called a Material Safety Data Sheet (MSDS). The MSDS for each hazardous chemical must be easy to find and use. Make sure you know where MSDSs are kept and how to find the information you need. You have a right to know—

- Which hazardous chemicals are in the facility.
- Where those chemicals are in the facility.
- What the specific dangers of those chemicals are.
- How to identify chemical hazards in your facility.
- How to protect yourself and others from being exposed to hazardous chemicals.
- What to do if you or others are exposed to such hazards.

Hazardous chemicals are not dangerous as long as they are handled and stored properly, as specified in the Hazard Communication Standard. Keep unauthorized personnel away from chemical storage areas. Think of all chemicals as dangerous and treat them carefully.

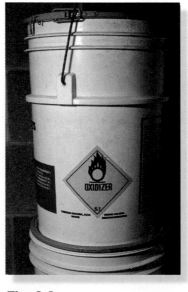

Fig. 2-9

Bloodborne Pathogens Standard

The federal Occupational Safety and Health Administration (OSHA) developed the Bloodborne Pathogens Standard to reduce the risk of disease spreading from one person to another. This standard helps protect you from contact with bodily fluids that may contain germs called bloodborne pathogens. Your facility management should help protect you from being exposed to germs that can cause disease and let you know what to do if an exposure occurs. Ask your lifeguarding instructor or check with your local American Red Cross for more information on bloodborne pathogens and prevention of disease transmission.

Local and State Regulations

Many local and state regulations also affect the operation of aquatic facilities, such as—

- Lifeguard certification requirements.
- Facility design and safety features.
- Pool capacities.
- Staff training requirements.
- Ratio of lifeguards to patrons.
- Water sanitation procedures.
- First aid equipment and supplies.
- Lifeguarding equipment.
- Diving depths.

Local and state regulations are specific to your area, so be sure to learn about those that affect your facility. Ask your manager for this information during orientation or in-service training.

Maintain Records and Reports

Facility management uses a variety of records and reports. The larger the facility, often the more records and reports it uses. Records and reports are important for the facility's daily operation. Records and reports at a facility may include—

- Employee schedules.
- Health, sanitation, and maintenance records.
- Daily attendance logs.
- In-service training records.
- Water conditions (pool temperature, clarity, chlorine and pH levels).
- Incident and injury reports.
- Time sheets.

Management will work with you to make sure that records and reports are filled out completely. Management will give you instructions for how and when to complete them and show you examples. Fill out forms on time, accurately, and thoroughly. Management then maintains the records and reports. Records and reports are used—

- To give information about equipment, personnel, procedures, and improvements.
- To give information about the cause and prevention of injuries.
- To comply with federal, state, and local laws requiring information about facility sanitation and maintenance.
- To document incidents.
- To protect the facility and its employees from possible legal actions.

Be sure to know what records and reports you need to fill out. You will learn these during orientation or in-service training or they will be in your facility's policies and procedures manual.

Assist After an Emergency

Management also has responsibilities after an emergency at the facility. Chapter 4 describes these responsibilities and the support management can provide for lifeguards involved in the incident. After an emergency, management is generally responsible for—

- Closing and reopening the pool.
- Interacting with the media.
- Reporting procedures.
- Helping lifeguards with problems related to the incident.

You can be comfortable knowing that management is there to support you on the job whenever an emergency happens.

Putting it All Together

The more you understand how injuries occur, the more you are able to prevent them. Good communication with patrons is important to help prevent injuries. Tell patrons about the potential for injury and educate them about the consequences of risky behavior. Enforce rules and regulations. These actions will help patrons have a safe and enjoyable experience. To prevent injuries, eliminate or reduce as many hazards as possible. Frequent safety checks help to control hazards. Facility surveillance, injury prevention, communication, and patron surveillance add up to a good overall approach for safety at your facility. Your own safety is important as well.

in review...

Circle the letter of the best answer or answers.

1. **The two injuries you are most concerned with preventing are—**
   a. Internal bleeding and head injuries.
   b. Spinal injuries and broken arms.
   c. Drowning and internal bleeding.
   d. Head, neck, or back injuries and drowning.

2. **Injury prevention strategies include—**
   a. Communication with patrons.
   b. Keeping fit.
   c. Facility safety checks.
   d. Strict adherence to rules.
   e. Patron surveillance.

3. **Injury prevention involves proper communication, which includes—**
   a. Informing patrons about the potential for injury.
   b. Talking with other lifeguards.
   c. Educating patrons about inappropriate behavior.
   d. Enforcing rules and regulations designed to prevent injury.
   e. Keeping an eye on troublemakers.

4. **Safety checks are conducted—**
   a. Before the facility opens.
   b. Periodically during the day.
   c. When the facility closes.
   d. Only when an incident occurs.

5. **When a potential hazard is found in a safety check—**
   a. Correct it right away.
   b. Write it down for the next shift to correct.
   c. Immediately close the entire facility.
   d. Fix it at your next break.

6. **Management's responsibilities include which of the following?**
   a. Warning patrons and staff about actual and potential dangers within the facility
   b. Addressing dangerous conditions
   c. Complying with all local, state, and federal regulations
   d. Keeping records on the facility and its employees
   e. Assisting after an emergency

7. **Facility management must give you what information about hazardous materials at the facility?**
   a. Where chemicals are located.
   b. How to identify hazardous chemicals.
   c. What to do if exposed to hazardous chemicals.
   d. How to order chemicals when the supply runs out.

Circle True or False

8. **People receive injury prevention information at swimming pools only from lifeguards.**

   True   False

9. **Weather affects the safety of swimmers both outdoors and indoors.**

   True   False

10. **Put in order the four steps of communication used to prevent a patron from engaging in risky behavior (Number from 1 to 4).**
    _____ Tell the person how he or she might be injured.
    _____ Explain to the person what the hazard or danger is.
    _____ Tell the person how to avoid being injured.
    _____ Get the person's attention.

chapter 3

patron
surveillance

The most important duty a lifeguard has is patron surveillance—keeping a close watch over the people in the facility. You will spend most of your time on patron surveillance. With effective surveillance you recognize behaviors or situations that may lead to life-threatening emergencies, such as drowning or injuries to the head, neck, or back.

Effective surveillance has four elements:

■ *Victim recognition*
■ *Proper scanning*
■ *Lifeguard stations*
■ *Area of responsibility*

FACT OR FICTION ACTIVITY

Are the following statements about drowning fact or fiction?

Directions: Read the following statments and place a checkmark in the correct column.

	Fact	Fiction
1. Active drowning victims always cry out for help.		
2. Active drowning victims stay straight up and down in the water while struggling.		
3. Active drowning victims use a kick, not their arms, to help keep themselves afloat.		
4. Active drowning victims struggle 20 to 60 seconds before submerging.		
5. Passive drowning victims are facedown and can be submerged or at the surface.		
6. Distressed swimmers and active drowning victims look very similar in the water.		

Victim Recognition

When you are conducting surveillance, look for behavior that indicates a swimmer is in distress or a person is drowning. You are more effective when you look for these behaviors because they are universal responses indicating that a patron is in trouble in the water. Your decision that a patron is in trouble must be based on his or her behavior, not on physical characteristics or appearance, such as age or ethnic or racial background.

You need to understand the behaviors that show when a victim is in distress or drowning. The table below compares the behaviors of a distressed swimmer and a drowning victim with those of a swimmer. Notice differences in—

- Breathing.
- Arm and leg action.
- Body position.
- Body propulsion or locomotion (movement) through the water.

Understanding these behaviors enables you to quickly recognize when someone needs your help. Your actions then can mean the difference between life and death for a distressed or drowning victim.

Active Drowning Victim

Active drowning victims have distinctive arm and body positions. They try to keep their mouths above the surface of the water. This universal behavior is called the instinctive drowning response[1]. This means that all active drowning victims have the same behaviors. An active drowning victim—

- Struggles to keep the face above water in an effort to breathe. If unable to do this, he or she begins to suffocate.
- Has arms extended to the side, pressing down for support.
- Has a vertical body position in the water with no supporting kick.
- May continue to struggle underwater.
- May eventually lose consciousness and stop moving.

An active drowning victim is struggling to breathe. His or her mouth repeatedly sinks below the surface and re-appears. While the mouth is below the surface, the

[1] Pia, F. "Observations on the Drowning of Nonswimmers" *Journal of Physical Education* (July 1974): 164-167.

Table 3-1   *Behaviors of Distressed Swimmers and Drowning Victims Compared to Swimmers*

	Swimmer	Distressed Swimmer	Active Drowning Victim	Passive Drowning Victim
	Fig. 3-1	Fig. 3-2	Fig. 3-3	Fig. 3-4
Breathing	Rhythmic breathing	Can continue breathing and may call for help	Struggles to breathe; cannot call out for help	Not breathing
Arm and leg action	Relatively coordinated	Floating, sculling, or treading water; may wave for help	Arms to sides alternately moving up and pressing down; no supporting kick	None
Body position	Horizontal	Horizontal or diagonal, depending on means of support	Vertical	Horizontal or vertical; face-down, face-up, or submerged
Locomotion	Recognizable	Little or no forward progress; less and less able to support self	None; has only 20-60 seconds before submerging	None

drowning victim keeps it closed to avoid swallowing water. When the mouth is above the surface, the drowning victim quickly exhales and then tries to inhale before the mouth goes below the surface again. While the victim is gasping for air, he or she also may take water into the mouth. Although some people believe active drowning victims can call out for help, this is not true. They can barely take in enough air to breathe, so there is no air left over to call out for help[2].

Passive Drowning Victim

A victim may progress from active to passive drowning or suddenly slip under water without a struggle. Passive drowning victims may float face-down at or near the surface or may sink to the bottom (Fig. 3-5). The victim may be unconscious because of—

- A heart attack or stroke.
- A head injury.
- A seizure.
- Hyperthermia (the body temperature becomes higher than normal).
- Hypothermia (the body cannot stay warm and the entire body cools).
- Hyperventilation (taking rapid deep breaths in rapid succession and forcefully exhaling).
- Use of alcohol and other drugs.

Fig. 3-5

Once a victim submerges and or loses consciousness, water can enter the trachea (windpipe). This causes a spasm of the vocal cords (laryngospasm), which blocks the airway to keep fluid or food out of the airway. Water may get into the lungs after submersion or loss of con-sciousness. Consider anyone you see who is submerged or floating facedown and motionless for 30 seconds to be a passive drowning victim. Check the victim's condition immediately. If the victim is conscious and was just holding his or her breath, explain why he or she should stop doing so.

The "RID Factor" as a Cause of Drowning

Most drownings happen when neither lifeguards nor other patrons notice the victim slip below the surface. A study of drownings in the United States from 1910 to 1980[3] showed that except for passive drownings, drownings in areas where lifeguards were on duty happened because of one or more of three causes, summarized as the *RID factor:*

- The failure of the lifeguard to **Recognize** the instinctive drowning response
- The **Intrusion** of secondary duties on the lifeguard's primary responsibility for patron surveillance
- **Distraction** from surveillance duties

Recognition

Knowing how to recognize that a swimmer is in distress or drowning is one of the most important lifeguarding skills. You must be able to tell their behavior from that of others who are swimming or playing safely in the water. You must recognize when someone needs to be rescued. Do not expect the victim or others to call you to the emergency.

Even when a victim slips underwater without a struggle, with good surveillance and scanning techniques, you can recognize someone lying motionless within seconds.

Intrusion

Intrusion happens when secondary duties, such as maintenance tasks, intrude on your primary responsibility of patron surveillance. Lifeguards often have to sweep the deck, empty trash barrels, pick up towels, check locker rooms, and perform other maintenance duties. While these duties may be part of your job, you should not do them while doing patron surveillance unless another lifeguard first takes over your assigned area of responsibility.

You cannot perform surveillance duties while coaching a team or teaching a lesson. The facility should have a separate lifeguard, coach, or instructor for these kinds of activities.

---

[2] Pia, Frank, *On Drowning,* Water Safety Films, Inc. (1970).
[3] Pia, F. "The RID Factor as a Cause of Drowning" *Parks and Recreation* (June 1984): 52-67.

Distraction

Distractions also will affect patron surveillance. This may include watching troublemakers on the deck for a lengthy period of time or talking with other lifeguards or friends. You might think a brief conversation is innocent, but during it you might miss a 20-60 second struggle of a young child. That child could die because you were distracted! You must not have social conversations while on duty.

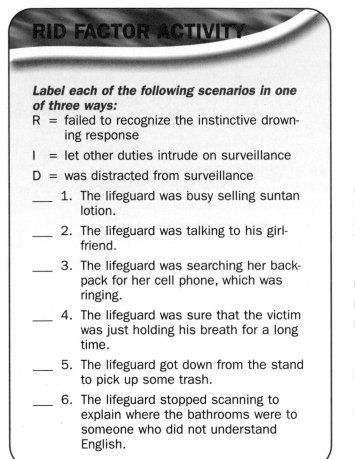

RID FACTOR ACTIVITY

Label each of the following scenarios in one of three ways:

R = failed to recognize the instinctive drowning response

I = let other duties intrude on surveillance

D = was distracted from surveillance

___ 1. The lifeguard was busy selling suntan lotion.

___ 2. The lifeguard was talking to his girlfriend.

___ 3. The lifeguard was searching her backpack for her cell phone, which was ringing.

___ 4. The lifeguard was sure that the victim was just holding his breath for a long time.

___ 5. The lifeguard got down from the stand to pick up some trash.

___ 6. The lifeguard stopped scanning to explain where the bathrooms were to someone who did not understand English.

Proper Scanning

Knowing how to recognize a victim in trouble in the water is the first step, but you also need to know how to scan effectively. Scanning is a visual technique for watching patrons in the water (Fig. 3-6). It is an active process. When you scan a swimming pool, you are not just passively watching patrons in the water. You actively observe their behavior and look for signals that someone in the water needs help.

Most of the time you are scanning, you use your peripheral vision. This is what you see at the edges of your vision. Peripheral vision detects motion and changes of patterns more easily than frontal vision (when you look right at something). Use your peripheral vision to detect

Fig. 3-6

something unusual, like the behaviors described for distressed swimmers and drowning victims. Then use your frontal vision to closely examine what your peripheral vision noticed.

Following are guidelines for effective scanning:

- Scan your assigned area of responsibility.
- Scan the bottom of the pool, as well as the surface.
- Scan thoroughly and repeatedly. Do not neglect any part of your area of responsibility, including any deck areas for which you are responsible.
- Scan from point to point, rapidly watching all movements of the patrons in your area.
- Scan for potential problems. Arm and leg action, body position, and movement through the water are good indicators of weak swimmers and those in trouble in the water.
- Spend less time and attention on patrons who are good swimmers or who are safely enjoying the water, but still include them in your scanning.
- Scan crowded areas carefully. Partially hidden arm movements may indicate that a victim is actively drowning.
- If a weak swimmer is slowly moving toward safety, check him or her more frequently while scanning your whole area of responsibility.
- If someone is attempting to swim but his or her body is vertical and the arms are paddling in front, he or she is not a good swimmer and should not be in deep water.
- While scanning, do not be distracted by people or activities. Keep focused on your area of responsibility.

- Do not interrupt scanning your area except to make a rescue or stop someone from breaking a rule. If you are the only lifeguard on duty and must stop someone from breaking a safety rule, do it quickly. Get the person's attention, explain the danger and how he or she can become injured, and, if necessary, how to avoid the injury. This should take only a few seconds, and you can often do it while still scanning the pool. If the patron needs a detailed explanation, call for assistance or tell the patron that you can discuss it further with him or her later when you take your break.

- Do not interrupt scanning your area if a patron asks you a question or has a suggestion or concern. Acknowledge the patron and explain quickly that you cannot look at him or her while talking, but you are still listening. Politely but briefly answer the patron's question, suggestion, or concern, or refer him or her to the head lifeguard, facility manager, or another staff member.

- Do not wait for patrons or other lifeguards to tell you that someone is drowning. A drowning victim is often surrounded by others who are unaware the drowning is happening right next to them. New lifeguards sometimes feel unsure of themselves and mistakenly wait for patrons or more experienced lifeguards to tell them that someone is in trouble.

- Be aware of areas that you cannot see or that are difficult to see. Areas may be blocked when patrons cluster together or from water movement, such as fountains or bubbles that block the view underwater. Adjust your body position to see into blind spots.

- Be careful of conditions that affect visibility, such as glare from the sun or overhead lights, cloudy water, or shadows on the water at different times of the day.

- Do not direct your attention to the scanning pattern itself, but stay focused on effective patron surveillance.

- Various factors affect scanning technique. Make adjustments for—
  - Your area of responsibility.
  - The type and location of your lifeguard station.
  - The variety of patron activities in your area.
  - Your own fatigue.

Lifeguard Stations

You may scan patrons from a lifeguard stand or from the deck. Both positions used together by different lifeguards often provide the best coverage.

Elevated Stations

Elevated lifeguard stations usually provide the most effective position for patron surveillance because they offer an excellent place for scanning your area of responsibility (Fig.3-7).

This is particularly important at a one-lifeguard facility where an elevated stand provides a much better view of patron activities than the view you have from a deck-level lifeguard station.

Keep the area under an elevated lifeguard stand clear at all times. Patrons in your way slow you down when getting to a person who needs help. Be sure to scan the area

EFFECTIVE SCANNING ACTIVITY

Mark the following statements about scanning guidelines as true or false:

1.	True	False	Scanning is best done with your peripheral vision.
2.	True	False	Scanning is best done with your frontal vision.
3.	True	False	Scan only the bottom of the pool.
4.	True	False	Scan your defined area of responsibility.
5.	True	False	Spend just as long scanning good swimmers as weak swimmers.
6.	True	False	Stop scanning so that you can make eye contact with patrons to whom you are giving information.
7.	True	False	If someone seems in trouble, watch that person's friends nearby to see if they call you for help.
8.	True	False	Pay attention to sun glare or shadows that affect visibility.
9.	True	False	Adjust your position as needed to eliminate blind spots.
10.	True	False	Encourage patrons to gather around your lifeguard stand so that they can help in an emergency.

Fig. 3-7

beneath your stand. Lifeguards on opposite sides of a pool can solve this problem by scanning below each other's stands. Position movable stands close to the edge of the pool with enough room to climb up and down from the stand.

Ground-level Stations

You may be assigned to a walking patrol, a fixed location on the deck, or a position in the water near a play structure (Fig. 3-8). In these positions, your view of the entire swimming area is limited, and patrons may be hidden from your view by play structures or other patrons.

While walking, face the patrons in your area of responsibility. Never turn your back on your area. The primary purpose of ground-level stations is to be close to patrons. Here you can easily make assists and enforce safety rules for patrons in the water and on the deck. While maintaining surveillance, you can also educate patrons the reasons behind the rules. But never let yourself become distracted from surveillance duties by talking socially with patrons.

Fig. 3-8

Lifeguard Rotations

Periodic rotations from one station to another, along with breaks, help keep you alert and less fatigued. Many things can make you feel fatigued:

- Dehydration
- Heat exhaustion
- Overexposure to the sun
- Making several rescues during your shift
- Lack of sleep

Follow these guidelines to help prevent fatigue:

- Drink lots of water.
- Use hats, sunglasses, and umbrellas.
- Come to work well rested.
- Rotate stations and take breaks.

Rotating from station to station also helps you learn conditions and hazards in the entire facility, instead of in just one location. Do not interrupt patron surveillance when rotating from one station to another. To relieve a lifeguard at a ground-level station, walk to the side of that lifeguard and begin scanning. Ask the lifeguard you are relieving whether any patrons in the area of responsibility need closer than normal supervision. Once you have started scanning, signal or tell the other lifeguard to go on break or to the next station.

To relieve a lifeguard at an elevated station—

1. Take a position next to the stand and begin scanning the area of responsibility. After a few moments of scanning, signal the lifeguard in the stand to climb down (Fig. 3-9A).

2. Once on the deck, this lifeguard takes a position next to the stand and resumes his or her surveillance of the area (Fig. 3-9B). Climb up in the stand and begin scanning.

3. Ask the lifeguard you are relieving whether any patrons in the area of responsibility need closer than normal supervision.

Fig. 3-9A

Fig. 3-9B

4. Signal or tell the outgoing lifeguard that he or she can leave.

You should take a break at least once an hour. In one system of surveillance, you may spend 20 or 30 minutes at one station, rotate to another station for 20 or 30 minutes, and then take a 20- or 30-minute break. In another system, you may spend 45 minutes at one stand, take a break for 15 minutes, and then go to another stand.

Do not make changes or substitutions in the schedule of rotations and breaks or leave the facility during a break without permission from the head lifeguard or manager.

If you are the only lifeguard on duty, you must clear the water during your break. Do not leave patrons in charge while you are on a break. The manager or another staff member should monitor the pool while you are on a break to prevent patrons from entering the water.

Area of Responsibility

The head lifeguard or the facility manager establishes each lifeguard's area of responsibility for patron surveillance. This may be total coverage (the whole pool or waterfront area) or zone coverage (only part of the pool or waterfront area). Another type of coverage is backup coverage, in which you take over part or all of a zone for another lifeguard who is making a rescue.

Total Coverage

Total coverage is used at single-lifeguard facilities or when only one lifeguard is needed for a small number of patrons present. If you are the only lifeguard on duty, you have to scan the entire area, rescue distressed swimmers or drowning persons, control the activities of patrons in and out of the water, and recognize and respond to other emergencies. If you find that you cannot provide adequate coverage for all patrons, tell your supervisor that you need help.

Zone Coverage

In zone coverage, the pool is divided into separate areas of responsibility for each lifeguard station (Fig. 3-10). Areas can be marked by ladders, lane lines, lifelines, visual markers, or the shape of the pool. Zone coverage is effective for high-risk areas and avoiding blind spots.

Zones should overlap by several feet so that the boundaries between them have double coverage. This prevents any area from not being scanned. You should know the zone for each guarding position.

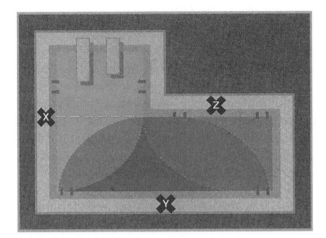

Fig. 3-10

Surveillance During Special Activities

People may come to your facility for a wide variety of aquatic activities. Patron surveillance for different activities involves different skills. The following sections describe surveillance for people in competitive events, swimming or diving lessons, and exercise or therapy.

Competitive Events

Participants in competitive events like swimming or diving meets, water polo games, and lifeguarding competitions usually have good aquatic skills, but they still deserve effective surveillance like anyone else. Adapt your scanning technique to their specific needs.

- Know and understand the rules and regulations for events you are lifeguarding and the safety policies for the competitive program.

- Plan how you would do a rescue if needed. For example, you cannot tow a victim across lane lines. Check the facility's emergency action plan (EAP) for how to remove a victim from the water when lane lines are in place. You should also know how to remove lane lines (and where the tool is kept) in case this is needed during a rescue. The same is true for boundary lines in water polo.

- Have swimmers follow the rules set for the lanes. For example, lanes are usually set for warm-up, sprinting, or practicing starts.

- If your pool has bulkheads, take a position where you can see both sides, or make sure there are enough lifeguards to scan both sides of the bulkhead. Do not allow swimmers under the bulkhead.

- At a diving well, know how to equalize pressure on your eardrums when you descend into very deep water. When you start to feel pressure, pinch your nostrils together and gently try to blow air out through your nose.

- In diving practices and competitions, watch for each diver to return to the surface. Take a position with a good view of the bottom.

Instructional or Therapeutic Activities

It is recommended that a lifeguard, in addition to the instructor, be present during swimming lessons and water exercise and water therapy classes. Follow these guidelines:

- Different precautions may be needed, depending on the age and ability of participants. Note how tall participants are and the water depth where they are practicing. Make sure nonswimmers do not enter water more than chest deep without their instructor.

- Be sure infants and young children are with a parent or other responsible adult while in the water.

- Watch for signs of any participant becoming fatigued.

- In therapy programs for people with medical conditions, be familiar with the conditions of the participants.

Putting it All Together

Patron surveillance is one of three ways to prevent injury. A lapse in coverage—even for just a few seconds—may lead to injury or death. To guard a facility, you must be able to recognize a distressed swimmer and an active or passive drowning victim. Effective scanning techniques and lifeguard stations are needed to locate people in trouble.

PUTTING IT ALL TOGETHER ACTIVITY

Directions: For the four categories listed across the top row, fill in the blanks to describe the breathing pattern, arm and leg action, body positions, and locomotion.

	Swimmer	Distressed Swimmer	Active Drowning Victim	Passive Drowning Victim
Breathing	Rhythmic breathing	Can continue breathing and may call for help	*sporatic*	Not breathing
Arm and leg action	*rhythmic*		Arms to sides alternately moving up and pressing down; no supporting kick	*no movement*
Body position	Horizontal	*horizontal vertical*	Vertical	
Locomotion		Little or no forward progress; less and less able to support self		None

in review...

Circle the letter of the correct answer or answers.

1. **The four elements of effective surveillance are—**
   a. Victim recognition.
   b. Proper scanning.
   c. Lifeguard stations.
   d. Effective sunglasses.
   e. Area of responsibility.
   f. Adherence to facility rules and regulations.

2. **To detect whether a swimmer is in distress, note the following behaviors:**
   a. Breathing.
   b. Physical condition.
   c. Arm and leg action.
   d. Body position.
   e. Age.
   f. Locomotion.

3. **You notice a person in the water whose body is diagonal and who can breathe and wave. The arms and legs are moving to keep the person's head above water, but there is no forward progress. This person is probably—**
   a. An active drowning victim who needs help.
   b. A passive drowning victim who needs help.
   c. A distressed swimmer who needs help.
   d. A beginning swimmer who does not need help.

4. **An active drowning person has four universal characteristics, called the instinctive drowning response. These are—**
   a. Struggles to keep the face above the water in an effort to breathe.
   b. Extends arms to the sides, pressing down for support.
   c. Calls or waves for help.
   d. A vertical body position in the water with no supporting kick.
   e. Struggles at the surface with no forward progress.
   f. A horizontal body position in the water.

5. **Which of the following describes a passive drowning victim?**
   a. Floating facedown and motionless.
   b. A horizontal body position but struggling to stay afloat.
   c. Body sinking to the bottom of the pool.
   d. Submerged and in a vertical body position.

6. **Passive drowning can result from various conditions or situations, including—**
   a. Hyperventilation.
   b. Hyperthermia.
   c. Alcohol use.
   d. Seizure.
   e. Heart attack or stroke.
   f. Head injury.

7. **The three causes of drownings summarized as the RID factor are—**
   a. Failure of the lifeguard to recognize the instinctive drowning response.
   b. Intrusion of secondary duties that interrupt the lifeguard's surveillance.
   c. Distraction from surveillance duties.
   d. Failure to reach the victim in time.

8. **Which statement is true about lifeguard rotation?**
   a. The lifeguard on duty goes to the break room to get his or her replacement.
   b. Both lifeguards scan during the rotation as one takes over for the other.
   c. The facility manager closes the pool during rotation.
   d. Lifeguards call out to each other to change positions when they both feel like it.

Circle True or False

9. **When scanning, use your frontal vision to detect the behaviors of distressed swimmers and drowning victims, and use your peripheral vision to closely examine behaviors.**

   True   False

Fill in the blanks.

10. **List at least three things that help prevent fatigue when you are lifeguarding:**

    _____

    _____

    _____

Facility Layouts and Emergency Action Plan Scenarios

#1

Facility:	6-lane 25-yard swimming pool, with diving area in the deep end.
Staff:	1 lifeguard and 1 cashier.
Attendance:	35 patrons.
Incident:	While climbing up the ladder to the high diving board, a 12-year-old patron loses her grip and falls to the ground. The patron has a possible fracture on the forearm as a result of the fall.

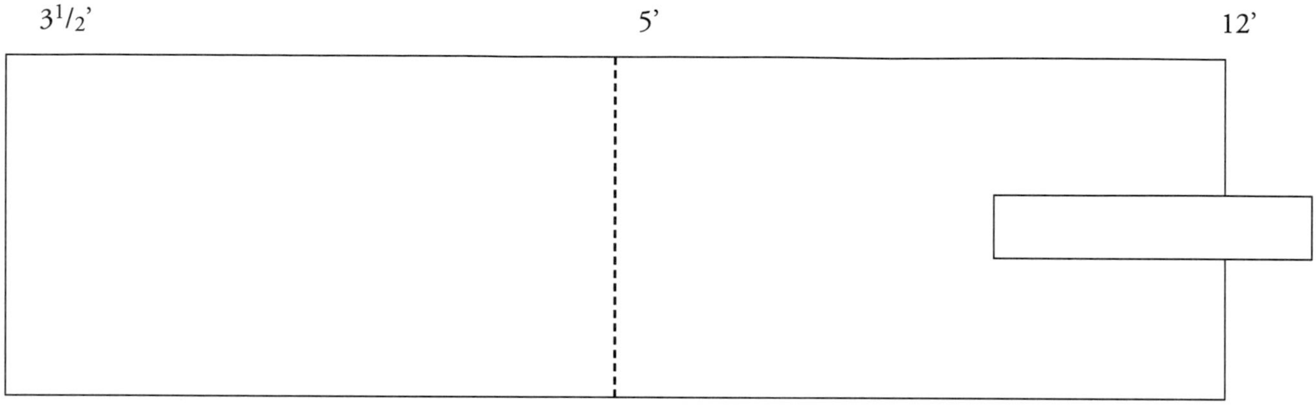

3½'   5'   12'

#2

Facility:	"L" shaped pool – 25 yards long with a diving well.
Staff:	3 lifeguards, 1 head lifeguard.
Attendance:	150 patrons.
Incident:	A frantic mother approaches a lifeguard at the stand and says that her 6-year-old son has disappeared. She last saw her child near the diving well 5 minutes ago.

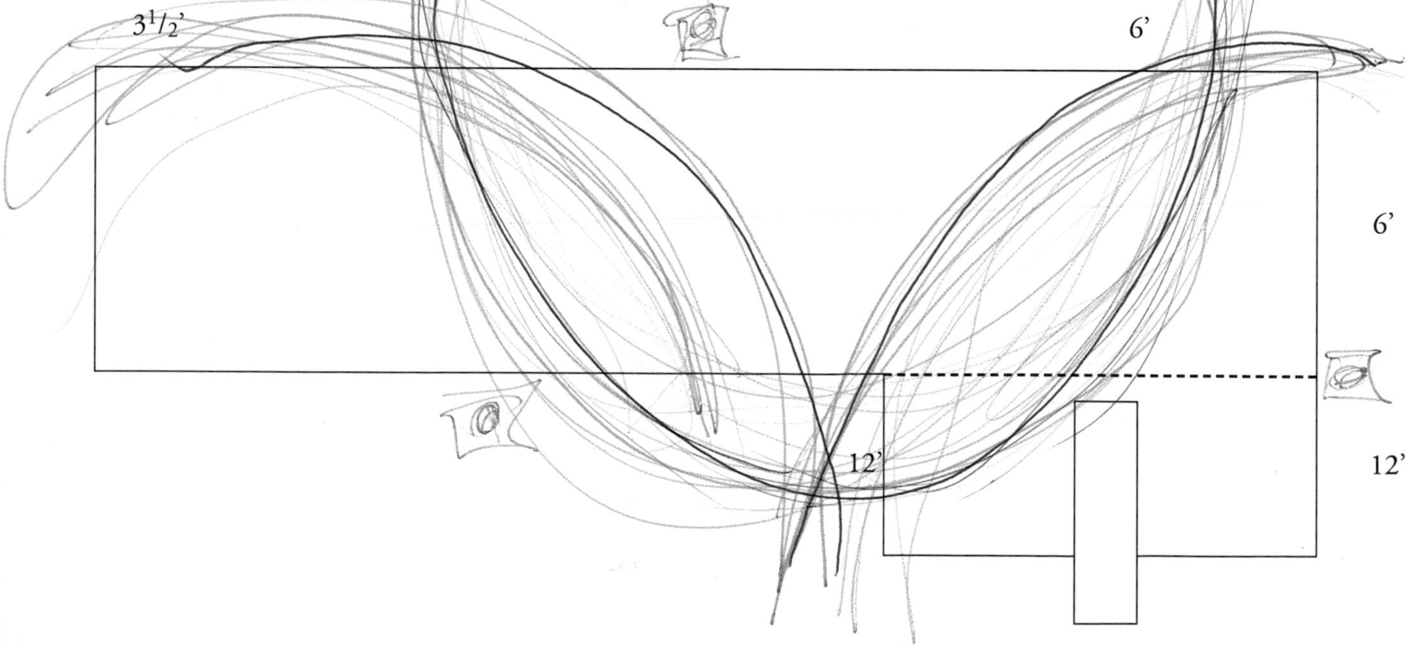

3½'   6'

6'

12'   12'

#3

Facility: "Z" shaped pool – 25 yards long with a diving well and a wading pool.

Staff: 4 lifeguards, 1 head lifeguard, and 1 manager.

Attendance: 175 patrons.

Incident: A 10-year-old boy runs and dives into the shallow end of the pool ($3^1/_2$ feet) and hits his head on the bottom. He does not surface.

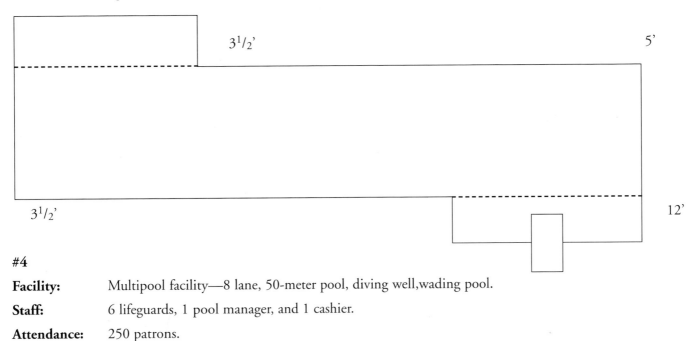

#4

Facility: Multipool facility—8 lane, 50-meter pool, diving well, wading pool.

Staff: 6 lifeguards, 1 pool manager, and 1 cashier.

Attendance: 250 patrons.

Accident: A middle-age lap swimmer is swimming laps in the 50-meter pool. Suddenly he stops swimming and clutches his chest. He submerges.

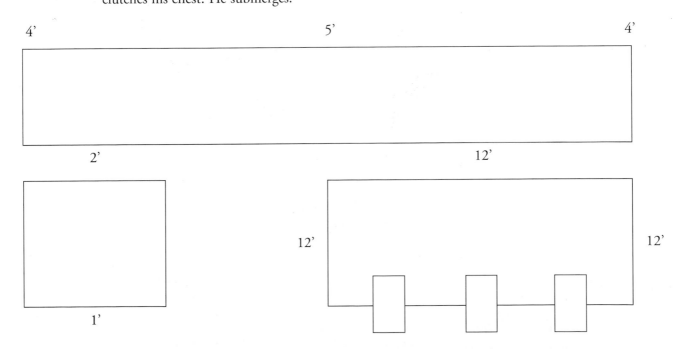

chapter 4

emergency
preparation

A serious incident can happen even when everyone works to prevent injuries. In an emergency, act as directed by the facility's emergency action plan(s). Be prepared to respond to emergencies like the following:

- *A young girl playing with her friends in the water starts to drown*
- *A person has a seizure, heart attack, or stroke and slips underwater*
- *A young man dives into shallow water, strikes his head, and becomes paralyzed*
- *The facility's power system suddenly fails*
- *A hazardous chemical spills, requiring the facility to be evacuated*
- *A severe lightning/thunderstorm is approaching your outdoor facility*

Responding to Emergencies

As a professional lifeguard, you are part of a safety team (Fig. 4-1). Also on the team are other lifeguards, managers, swimming instructors, security guards, concession staff, bystanders, and emergency medical services (EMS) personnel. Even if you are the only lifeguard on duty, others will help in an emergency. With guidance, bystanders too can help. They can control a crowd, relay a message to other team members, get equipment or supplies, or call EMS. You must know who is on your team and what actions you are to take in an emergency.

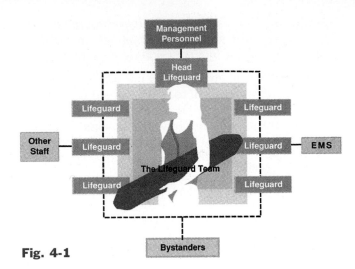

Fig. 4-1

Safety Team Responsibilities

When everyone on the team knows his or her responsibilities, the team works together effectively. Responsibilities of the members of the safety team may include—

- Following the emergency action plan(s).
- Calling EMS.
- Performing or assisting with a rescue.
- Providing back-up coverage.
- Controlling bystanders.
- Clearing the pool or facility.

Staff must know where equipment is kept, including the first aid kit, resuscitation mask, oxygen, and backboard. The emergency action plan states who gets the equipment and how to get it to the injured victim.

Emergency Action Plans (EAPs)

Emergency action plans (EAPs) are detailed plans for how everyone acts in emergencies. Emergency action plans should be in the facility's policies and procedures manual. Learn and practice your assigned responsibilities in the EAPs during orientation and in-service training. All EAPs should be practiced often to develop teamwork.

Emergency Action Plan Steps

A sample EAP for an emergency in the water or on land includes the following steps:

1. **Lifeguard recognizes that someone needs immediate help.**

   The lifeguard recognizes an emergency in the water or on land.

2. **Lifeguard activates EAP.**

   Before leaving a station, the lifeguard first activates the EAP by giving a prearranged signal, such as a whistle blast, to alert other lifeguards and staff. They can

provide back-up coverage, give additional help, and call EMS personnel if necessary.

3. **Lifeguard follows the General Rescue Procedures for emergencies that occur in the water or on land.**

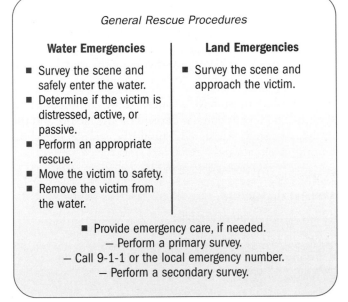

General Rescue Procedures

Water Emergencies
- Survey the scene and safely enter the water.
- Determine if the victim is distressed, active, or passive.
- Perform an appropriate rescue.
- Move the victim to safety.
- Remove the victim from the water.

Land Emergencies
- Survey the scene and approach the victim.

- Provide emergency care, if needed.
  – Perform a primary survey.
  – Call 9-1-1 or the local emergency number.
  – Perform a secondary survey.

4. **Chain of command notified.**

   The lifeguard who made the rescue notifies the head lifeguard or facility manager. With a serious injury or death, the head lifeguard or facility manager notifies the appropriate supervisor(s) as soon as possible. The supervisor contacts the victim's family.

5. **Witnesses interviewed.**

   As soon as possible, the designated safety team member interviews witnesses who saw the incident. Interviews are done privately and documented in writing.

6. **Reports completed.**

   The lifeguard(s) who made the rescue fills out an incident report as soon as possible. Other lifeguards and other staff involved in the incident must also fill out an incident report form.

7. **Equipment checked.**

   The lifeguard checks the equipment and supplies used in the rescue. Any damaged or missing items are reported or replaced. If the facility was cleared during the incident, all required equipment must be back in place before reopening the facility.

8. **Corrective action taken.**

   Any situation that may have contributed to the incident is corrected before the facility is reopened or as soon as possible. If needed, restrict access to any unsafe area.

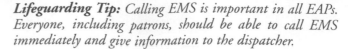

9. Follow-up staff discussion.

If the incident involved a serious injury or death, a professional may help facility personnel and lifeguards cope with the experience.

During an Emergency

When you recognize an emergency, first signal other lifeguards and staff. Your signal tells other lifeguards that you are involved in an emergency and that they should cover your area (back-up coverage). If you are the only lifeguard on duty, signal patrons to leave the pool.

Every facility must have a safety team communication system. The signals you use depend on the facility and the number of staff. All signals should be simple and clear. Common signals are—

- Whistles.
- Hand signals.
- Rescue equipment signals.
- Public address systems.
- Phones.
- Two-way radios.
- Flags.

Calling EMS

Many areas have a 9-1-1 emergency telephone system for calling EMS. In some communities, a local number is used. In some facilities, you must dial 8 or 9 first for an outside line. Emergency numbers should be posted on or near all telephones, along with the information to give the EMS dispatcher (Fig. 4-2). Wasting minutes to find the emergency number could cost a life.

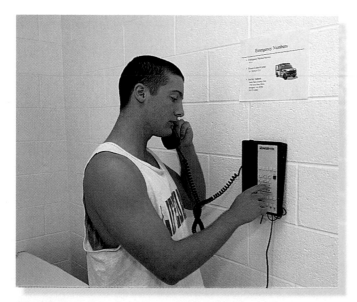

Fig. 4-2

Lifeguarding Tip: Calling EMS is important in all EAPs. Everyone, including patrons, should be able to call EMS immediately and give information to the dispatcher.

If you decide a victim's injury is not serious and EMS does not need to be called, use your first aid training and follow facility procedures. Decide whether the person can or should not go back in the water. In some cases, you may recommend that the person should see a doctor.

Controlling Bystanders

One of your responsibilities in an emergency may be controlling bystanders so that first aid can be given. Controlling bystanders may involve—

- Using a firm but calm voice to ask bystanders to move back so that care can be given. Do not yell at patrons.
- Roping off areas or positioning chairs around the emergency site.
- Recruiting bystanders so they can assist lifeguards and facility staff in crowd control.
- Using the public address system to help control bystanders.
- Repeating your commands and requests as often as necessary.
- Clearing a path for EMS personnel, and telling the crowd to make room to let them through.
- Keeping bystanders and any children away from the water's edge if the pool is cleared.

After an Emergency

After an injured victim is cared for and turned over to EMS personnel, you and other members of the safety team still have several tasks to complete.

Completing Reports

After the injured victim has been released or transported by EMS personnel, lifeguards and other staff involved in the incident must fill out an incident report form (see Sample Incident Report Form on pages 38-39). Write down only factual information, not your personal opinion or anything you heard from someone else.

Witness statements may also be required. Getting a statement or witnesses' names, addresses, and phone numbers may be your responsibility, although usually a head lifeguard or facility manager does this. Witnesses write their statements on separate, dated forms. They describe the incident in their own words. Lifeguards and other staff should not tell witnesses what to say in this statement.

Checking Equipment

All equipment and first aid supplies used in the emergency must be replaced. Use your facility's safety checklist to check equipment and supplies. If the injured victim was put on a backboard, EMS personnel likely kept the backboard while transporting the victim to a hospital. If that happens, ask EMS personnel to temporarily exchange backboards with your facility. Otherwise, the backboard must be immediately replaced or the facility closed until the backboard is returned. Report other missing or damaged items to the head lifeguard.

Reopening the Facility

After a significant incident, the head lifeguard or manager decides whether to close the facility temporarily and when to reopen. The decision may depend on whether enough lifeguards are ready to go back to surveillance and all the required equipment is in place. Lifeguards must tell their supervisors if they are too upset by the incident to do a good job of surveillance.

Staff Debriefing

This meeting usually is held after incident reports are filled out. The entire safety team attends. The staff talk about what happened before, during, and after the emergency. Goals of the debriefing are to—

- Examine what happened.
- Assess the effectiveness of the EAP.
- Consider new ways to prevent similar incidents in the future.
- Avoid assigning blame or criticizing everyone's actions.
- Be alert for critical incident stress reactions.

COMPONENTS OF AN EMERGENCY ACTION PLAN ACTIVITY

Directions: Use the scenario assigned by your lifeguarding instructor on pages 30-31 ("Facility Layouts and Emergency Action Plan Scenarios") to answer the following questions)

COMPONENTS	QUESTIONS TO ANSWER
Staff assignments and responsibilities	How should all staff respond?
	Who covers the vacant lifeguard zone?
	What is the role of each staff member?
	How many lifeguards respond to the victim?
	Who meets and escorts EMS personnel to the victim?
Providing first aid	Who gets the first aid kit?
	Who gets the backboard, if needed?
Communications	What signals are used to notify staff of an emergency?
Interacting with the public	Who is responsible for bystanders?
	Who is responsible for interacting with the media, the victim's family, and health department officials?
Completing reports	Who completes the report?
	Is there a standard incident form to fill out? If so, where is it?
	When does the form need to be completed?

Dealing with Questions

Television or newspaper reporters, insurance company representatives, attorneys, and just curious people may ask you questions about the emergency. Do not give out any information about an injured person. Only management or a designated spokesperson should talk to the media or others about an incident. Talking about what happened can lead to legal action. The procedure for dealing with the media and others should be in the policies and procedures manual and the EAP. If people ask you questions, tell them to talk to the manager or spokesperson. Do not discuss the emergency with anyone outside the facility, except for counselors helping you cope with it. If the area where the incident happened is visible from public property, you cannot stop someone from taking a picture from a public area. Anyone who asks to take a photo in the facility, however, needs permission from management.

Critical Incident Stress

In an emergency, your body reacts in several ways. Your muscles tense, your heart rate and breathing increases, and other body reactions occur. The stress of the emergency can cause distress or disruption in your mental or emotional balance. The stress can cause sleeplessness, anxiety, depression, exhaustion, restlessness, nausea, nightmares, and other problems. Some effects may happen right away, but others may appear days, weeks, or even months after the incident. People react to stress in different ways, even with the same incident. You may not even recognize that you are suffering from stress or know its cause.

A critical incident causes a strong emotional reaction and hurts one's ability to cope and function after the incident. For lifeguards, critical incidents include—

- Any patron's death, especially the death of a child or one following a prolonged rescue attempt.
- An event that endangers the rescuer's life or threatens someone important to the rescuer.
- The death of a co-worker on the job.
- Any powerful emotional event, especially one that receives media coverage.

Rescues involving severe injury or death are stressful for lifeguards. Rescues are especially stressful if a lifeguard feels he or she did something wrong or failed to do something—even after doing exactly what he or she was trained to do.

This stress is called critical incident stress. It is a normal reaction. Someone experiencing this usually needs help to recognize it, understand it, and cope with it. If you do not identify and learn to manage stress, it can also disrupt your personal life and your effectiveness on the job.

Critical incident stress debriefing (CISD) is a way trained professionals help someone suffering from this kind of stress. The job of a CISD counselor is to help everyone involved in a stressful incident talk about what happened and express his or her feelings and reactions. He or she helps everyone acknowledge their feelings, recognize them as normal, and learn how to cope with them. Facility management can help you by contacting a CISD counselor.

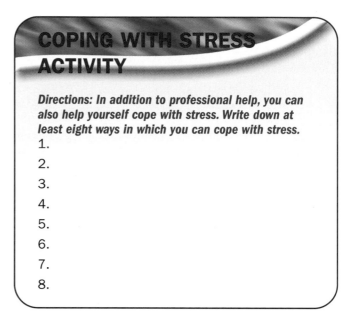

COPING WITH STRESS ACTIVITY

Directions: In addition to professional help, you can also help yourself cope with stress. Write down at least eight ways in which you can cope with stress.

1.
2.
3.
4.
5.
6.
7.
8.

Putting it All Together

Emergency action plans are blueprints for handling emergencies. Your skills, teamwork, in-service training, and practice of EAPs all help you know how to act in an emergency and manage the stress it may cause.

in review...

Circle the letter of the best answer or answers.

1. **Whom of the following could be included on a safety team?**
   a. Lifeguards
   b. Security guards
   c. Facility management
   d. Swimming instructors
   e. Bystanders

2. **With guidance, untrained bystanders can help in which of the following ways during an emergency?**
   a. Controlling the crowd
   b. Calling for additional help
   c. Getting equipment and supplies
   d. Taking over surveillance for the lifeguard.

3. **After an incident, which of the following might be a responsibility of a lifeguard?**
   a. Controlling bystanders.
   b. Deciding if you are able to return to work.
   c. Filling out an incident report form.
   d. Checking and reporting any missing items to management.

4. **Which of the following are acceptable steps in crowd control?**
   a. Rope off the area.
   b. Yell at patrons if necessary.
   c. Recruit any bystanders you may need.
   d. Direct those not helping you to back away from the victim.

5. **Which of the following are acceptable purposes for a staff debriefing?**
   a. To compare notes.
   b. To get a complete picture of what occurred.
   c. To prepare emergency plans and eliminate or minimize hazards.
   d. To assign blame or criticize.
   e. To generate material for a thorough report of the incident.
   f. To prepare information for everyone to give to the media.

6. **Which of the following critical incidents might a lifeguard encounter?**
   a. The death of a co-worker on the job.
   b. The death of a child.
   c. The death of any victim.
   d. An event that is particularly threatening to the rescuer.

7. **The purpose of a critical incident stress debriefing is to—**
   a. Help everyone involved talk about what happened and express their feelings and reactions.
   b. Help everyone learn to acknowledge their feelings and recognize them as a normal result of the incident.
   c. Help everyone involved figure out what went wrong and who was responsible.
   d. Help everyone learn ways to cope with the feelings that result from the incident.

Circle True or False.

8. **Critical incident stress is an abnormal reaction after a stressful situation.**

   True   False

9. **The best and quickest way to activate the emergency action plan is to yell loudly for help.**

   True   False

10. **Sequence the following steps a lifeguard should take when responding to an emergency (Number 1-8).**
    ___ Activate emergency action plan.
    ___ Provide emergency care if needed.
    ___ Recognize that someone needs immediate help.
    ___ Perform an appropriate rescue.
    ___ Determine if the victim is distressed, active, or passive.
    ___ Survey the scene and safely enter the water.
    ___ Remove the victim from the water.
    ___ Move the victim to safety.

SAMPLE INCIDENT REPORT FORM

Date of Report: _____   Date of Incident: _____   Time of Incident: _____ AM   PM

Facility Information:

Facility: _____   Phone number: (   ) _____

Address: _____ City _____ State _____ Zip _____

Personal Data — Injured Party

Name: _____ Age: _____ Gender: ____ Male ____ Female

Address: _____ City _____ State _____ Zip _____

Phone Number(s):   Home (   ) _____   Work (   ) _____

Family Contact (Name and Phone number): _____ (   ) _____

Incident Data

Location of Incident: _____

_____

Description of Incident: _____

_____

_____

Did an injury occur?   ____ Yes   ____ No

If yes, describe the type of injury: _____

_____

_____

Witnesses

1. Name: _____   Phone number: (   ) _____

   Address: _____ City _____ State _____ Zip _____

   Witness description of incident: _____

2. Name: _____   Phone number: (   ) _____

   Address: _____ City _____ State _____ Zip _____

   Witness description of incident: _____

SAMPLE INCIDENT REPORT FORM—cont'd

Care Provided

Did victim refuse medical attention by staff? ____ Yes ____ No

Did facility staff provide care? ____ Yes ____ No

Name of person that provided care: _____

Describe in detail care given: _____

_____

_____

_____

Was EMS called? ____ Yes ____ No   If yes, by whom? _____

Time EMS called: A.M.   P.M.

Was the victim transported to an emergency facility? ____ Yes ____ No

If yes, where? _____ If no, person returned to activity? ____ Yes ____ No

If the victim is a minor — Were the minor's parent's contacted (if not present)? ____ Yes ____ No

Victim's signature (Parent's/Guardian's if victim is a minor): _____

Facility Data

Number of lifeguards on duty at time of incident: ____ Number of patrons in facility at time of incident: ____

Weather condition at time of incident: _____

Water condition at time of incident: _____

Deck condition at time of incident: _____

Name(s) of lifeguard(s) involved in incident: _____

Report Prepared By:

Name: _____   Position: _____

Signature: _____   Date: _____

chapter 5

rescue
skills

As a lifeguard, you may often enter the water to make rescues. After determining that the victim needs help, check his or her condition and use an appropriate rescue skill. The skills in this chapter can be used in most aquatic environments, although you may have to modify them in some situations.

General Procedures for a Water Emergency

In all rescue situations, activate the emergency action plan (EAP) (Fig. 5-1), use rescue equipment, provide for your own safety and the safety of the victim you are rescuing, and follow these general procedures:

1. **Survey the scene and safely enter the water.** Choose the best entry based on—
   - Water depth.
   - Your height above the water.
   - Location of the victim.
   - Facility design.
2. **Determine if the victim is distressed, active, or passive.** Determine whether the victim is a distressed swimmer or an active or passive drowning victim and whether the victim is at the surface or submerged.
3. **Perform an appropriate rescue.** Swim to the victim to make contact and perform a rescue. Use an appropriate rescue based on the victim's condition.
4. **Move the victim to safety.** Move the victim to the side of the pool or pier or to the shoreline. The kick you use to move the victim to safety depends on your strength and ability.
5. **Remove the victim from the water.** Use the appropriate removal technique depending on the victim's condition and the facility's design.
6. **Give emergency care as needed.** Depending upon the victim's condition, you may have to give rescue breathing, CPR, or other care until EMS personnel arrive.

Fig. 5-1

The Rescue Tube

The rescue tube makes the rescue safer for both the lifeguard and the victim. It is a 45- to 54-inch tube with an attached tow line and shoulder strap. The rescue tube—

- Helps you and the victim stay afloat.
- Keeps the victim's mouth above water. This causes less anxiety and makes it easier for the victim to follow your directions.
- Makes it easier to move the victim to safety.
- Lessens the chances of the victim grabbing you during the rescue.

Rescue Readiness

When performing patron surveillance, always keep your rescue tube ready to use.

- Keep the strap of the rescue tube over your shoulder and neck.
- Hold the rescue tube across your thighs when sitting in a lifeguard chair or across your stomach when standing.
- Hold the excess line in one hand to keep it from getting caught in the chair or other equipment as you start the rescue.

Lifeguarding Tip: Always have your rescue tube ready for use when performing patron surveillance.

Entries

There are two safe ways to enter the water for a rescue.

Stride jump

Use the stride jump with a rescue tube only if the water is at least 5 feet deep and you are no more than 3 feet above the water.

1. Squeeze the rescue tube high against your chest with the tube under your armpits.
2. Hold the excess line in one hand to keep it from getting caught in the lifeguard chair or other equipment when you jump into the water (Fig. 5-2A).
3. Leap into the water with one leg forward and the other leg back (Fig. 5-2B).
4. Lean slightly forward, with your chest ahead of your hips, and focus on the victim as you enter the water.
5. Squeeze or scissor your legs together for upward thrust (Fig. 5-2C).
6. Focus on the victim and begin your approach (Fig. 5-2D).

Fig. 5-2A

Fig. 5-2B

Fig. 5-2C

Fig. 5-3A

Fig. 5-2D

Compact jump

Use the compact jump when you are more than 3 feet above the water, such as on a lifeguard stand, but do it only into water at least 5 feet deep. You can also use the compact jump from the deck into water less than 5 feet deep.

Fig. 5-3B

1. Squeeze the rescue tube high against your chest with the tube under your armpits.

2. Hold the excess line in one hand to keep it from getting caught in the lifeguard chair or other equipment when you jump into the water (Fig. 5-3A).

3. Jump out and away from the lifeguard chair or pool deck.

4. Bend your knees and keep your feet together and flat to absorb the shock if you hit bottom. Do not point your toes or keep your legs straight or stiff (Fig. 5-3B).

5. Let the buoyancy of the rescue tube bring you back to the surface.

6. Focus on the victim when you surface, and begin your approach (Fig. 5-3C).

Fig. 5-3C

Rescue Approaches

The best way to swim to the victim is with a modified crawl or breaststroke (Fig. 5-4A-B). Keep the rescue tube under your armpits or torso, and swim toward the victim with your head up. Keep the rescue tube in control at all times.

Lifeguarding Tip: If the rescue tube slips out from under your arms or torso while you are swimming to the victim, let

Fig. 5-5

Fig. 5-4A

Fig. 5-6A

Fig. 5-4B

it trail behind you. Slow down and reposition the tube before contacting the victim.

Fig. 5-6B

Rescues at or Near the Surface

Use the following skills to rescue a distressed swimmer or an active drowning victim at or near the surface of the water.

Extension assist from the deck

The safest way to help is to stay on a deck and reach out a rescue tube to a distressed swimmer who is close to the side of the pool or a pier.

1. Take the shoulder strap off your shoulder.
2. Hold the shoulder strap in your hand, and reach out to the distressed swimmer with the rescue tube in your other hand (Fig. 5-5).
3. Tell the victim to grab the rescue tube.
4. Slowly pull him or her to safety.

Swimming extension rescue

The swimming extension rescue works well for a distressed swimmer.

1. Approach the victim from the front (Fig. 5-6A).
2. Hold out the end of the rescue tube to the distressed swimmer (Fig. 5-6B).
3. Tell the victim to hold the rescue tube and kick if he or she can.
4. Pull the victim to safety.

Active drowning victim rear rescue

The active drowning victim rear rescue can be used for either a distressed swimmer or an active drowning victim.

1. Approach the victim from behind (Fig 5-7A).

2. Reach under the victim's armpits and grasp his or her shoulders (Fig. 5-7B).

3. Squeeze the rescue tube between your chest and the victim's back (Fig. 5-7C).

4. Keep your head to one side of the victim's head to avoid being hit by it if it moves backward.

5. Lean back and pull the victim onto the rescue tube (Fig. 5-7D).

Fig. 5-7A

Fig. 5-7B

Fig. 5-7C

Fig. 5-7D

6. Use the rescue tube to support the victim with his or her mouth out of the water.

7. Talk to calm him or her.

8. Move the victim to safety.

Lifeguarding Tip: When making a rescue, always keep control of your rescue tube. If it slips out, put the rescue tube back in place before contacting the victim.

Passive drowning victim rear rescue

Use the passive drowning victim rear rescue when the victim is at or near the surface but seems unconscious and you do not think he or she has a spinal injury. If you suspect a head, neck, or back injury, use the techniques described in Chapter 8. The victim may be floating face-down at or near the surface in a vertical to horizontal position. Your goal is to put the rescue tube under the victim's shoulders or back to support him or her face-up:

1. Approach the victim from behind.

2. Reach under the victim's armpits and grasp his or her shoulders (Fig. 5-8A).

3. Squeeze the rescue tube between your chest and the victim's back.

4. Keep your head to one side of the victim's head to avoid being hit by it if it moves backward.

Fig. 5-8A

5. Roll the victim over so that he or she is face-up on top of the rescue tube (Fig. 5-8B)

6. Move the victim to safety. For greater distances, use one hand to stroke. Reach your right arm over the victim's right shoulder and grasp the rescue tube. Then use your left hand to stroke. Or reach with your left arm and stroke with your right hand (Fig. 5-8C).

Fig. 5-8B

Fig. 5-8C

Rescuing a Submerged Victim

Sometimes a drowning victim is below the surface and beyond your reach. This may occur when nonswimmers or very weak swimmers enter water over their head. A victim may also submerge after a heart attack, stroke, or seizure or otherwise become unconscious in the water.

Feet-first surface dive

With a surface dive, you go underwater to rescue or search for a submerged victim:

1. Swim to the point over the victim. Let go of your rescue tube but keep the strap around your shoulders.

2. In a vertical position, press down with your hands and kick strongly to raise your body out of the water.

3. Take a breath with your arms at your sides and let your body sink underwater. Keep your legs straight and together with your toes pointed.

4. As your downward momentum slows, turn your palms outward and sweep your hands and arms upward.

5. Repeat this arm movement until you are deep enough.

Submerged victim rescue

A submerged victim may be passive or active. Use the same rescue skill in both cases:

1. Do a feet-first surface dive, and position yourself behind the victim (Fig. 5-9A).

2. Reach one arm under the victim's arm (right arm to right side or left arm to left side) and across the victim's chest. Hold firmly onto the victim's opposite side (Fig. 5-9B).

Fig. 5-9A

Fig. 5-9B

3. When you have the victim, reach up above your shoulder with your other hand and grasp the towline. Pull it down and hold it in the same hand holding the victim (Fig. 5-9C). Keep pulling it in this way until you reach the surface. As you surface, position the rescue tube so that it is squeezed between your chest and the victim's back (Fig. 5-9D).

4. Reach your free arm over the tube and under the victim's armpit. Grasp his or her shoulder (right arm to right shoulder or left arm to left shoulder) (Fig. 5-9E).

5. Move your other arm from across the victim's chest, and grasp his or her shoulder.

6. Hold the victim in a face-up position on the rescue tube (Fig. 5-9F).

7. Move the victim quickly to safety.

Fig. 5-9E

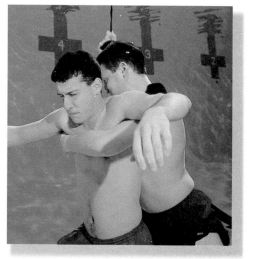

Fig. 5-9C

Fig. 5-9F

Fig. 5-9D

Lifeguarding Tips: Depending on how deep the victim is, use one of these techniques:

- *If you can reach the victim without removing the strap, continue the rescue.*

- *If you have to take off the strap to descend, hold onto it so that you can use the rescue tube to help bring the victim to the surface.*

- *If the victim is deeper than the tow line reaches, let go of the strap, grasp the victim, and kick to the surface. When you return to the surface, place the rescue tube in position behind the victim and continue the rescue.*

- *If you let go of the strap of your rescue tube, you might not be able to reach it when you surface. The side of the pool or pier may be closer than the rescue tube. In this situation, move to safety without the rescue tube. Support the victim in a face-up position, and if possible, call for help from another lifeguard.*

Escapes

A distressed swimmer or a drowning victim may grab you if your technique is faulty or the rescue tube slips out of position. Always hold onto your rescue tube because it helps both the victim and you stay afloat. If you lose your rescue tube and are grabbed by a drowning victim, use either the front or rear head-hold escape. To perform a front head-hold escape:

1. As soon as you are grabbed, take a quick breath, tuck your chin down, turn your head to either side, and raise your shoulders. (Fig. 5-10A).

2. Once underwater, bring your hands up to the victim's elbows or to the undersides of the victim's arms just above the elbows. Push hard up and away from you. Keep your chin tucked, your arms fully extended, and your shoulders raised until you are free (Fig. 5-10B).

3. Quickly swim out of reach. Reposition your rescue tube, use a rear approach, and try the rescue again (Fig. 5-10C).

Fig. 5-10C

To perform a rear head-hold escape:

1. If the victim grabs you from behind, take a quick breath, tuck your chin down, turn your head to either side, and raise your shoulders. Submerge with the victim. You may need to perform a feet first surface dive to do this (Fig. 5-11A).

2. Once underwater, bring your hands up to the victim's elbows or to the undersides of the victim's arms just above the elbows. Push hard up and away from you while twisting your head and shoulders. Keep your chin tucked, your arms fully extended, and your shoulders raised until you are free (Fig. 5-11B).

Fig. 5-10A

Fig. 5-10B

Fig. 5-11A

Fig. 5-11B

Fig. 5-11C

3. Quickly swim out of reach. Reposition your rescue tube, use a rear approach, and try the rescue again (Fig. 5-11C).

Multiple-Victim Rescue

Sometimes two or more victims need to be rescued. A victim may grab a nearby swimmer to try to stay above the water. Several lifeguards should perform a multiple-victim rescue if possible. At least one lifeguard should check the bottom for possible submerged victims while other lifeguards rescue victims at the surface.

If you are the only lifeguard rescuing two victims who are clutching each other—

1. Approach one victim from behind (Fig. 5-12A).

2. Reach under the victim's armpits, and grasp his or her shoulders. Squeeze the rescue tube between your chest and the victim's back. Keep your head to one side of the victim's head (Fig. 5-12B).

3. Use the rescue tube to support both victims with their mouths out of the water. Talk to the victims to help calm them.

4. Support both victims until other lifeguards arrive or the victims calm down enough to help reach safety (Fig. 5-12C).

Fig. 5-12A

Fig. 5-12B

Fig. 5-12C

Lifeguarding Tip: The buoyancy of the rescue tube will keep you and the victims afloat until other lifeguards arrive. Calm the victims and continue to support them on the rescue tube. Once they calm down, they may be able to help you move to safety.

Removal From Water

A victim who is unconscious or too exhausted may need to be removed from the water. Your decision to remove the victim depends on the victim's condition and size, how soon you expect help to arrive, and whether anyone can help you. Two lifeguards or one lifeguard and a bystander are needed to safely remove a victim from the water. If a victim needs first aid, rescue breathing, or CPR, remove him or her from the pool immediately and have someone call EMS.

To perform the two-person removal from water using a backboard—

1. The primary lifeguard brings the victim to the side of the pool and turns him or her to face the deck.

2. The assisting lifeguard or bystander on deck grabs the victim's opposite wrists and pulls the victim up slightly to keep the head above the water and away from the pool edge. Support the victim's head so that it does not fall forward (Fig. 5-13A).

Fig. 5-13A

Fig. 5-13C

Fig. 5-13B

Fig. 5-13D

3. The primary lifeguard removes the rescue tube and climbs out of the water. He or she gets a backboard and removes the head immobilizer and the straps (if possible).

4. The primary lifeguard guides the backboard, foot-end first, straight down into the water next to the victim (Fig. 5-13B). The assisting lifeguard or bystander then turns the victim onto the backboard (Fig. 5-13C). Each rescuer then quickly grasps one of the victim's wrists and one of the handholds of the backboard.

5. When the primary lifeguard gives the signal, both rescuers pull the backboard and victim onto the deck, resting the underside of the board against the edge of the pool. (Remember to lift with your legs and not with your back). Step backward and then lower the backboard onto the deck (Fig. 5-13D).

6. Provide immediate care based on the victim's condition. For example, if the victim is unconscious and not breathing, give rescue breathing. Continue care until EMS arrives and takes over.

Putting it All Together

Different rescue skills are needed for distressed swimmers and active or passive drowning victims. Special skills are also needed for submerged victims. Although rescuing the person safely is the goal, never jeopardize your own safety. Always use a rescue tube to keep you and the drowning victim safe. Once the victim has been brought to safety, remove the victim from the water and give first aid as needed.

in review...

Circle the letter of the best answer or answers.

1. **Which of the following statements are true about rescue tubes?**
   a. Rescue tubes keep the victim and you afloat.
   b. Rescue tubes make it easier to move the victim to safety.
   c. Rescue tubes help reduce the chance that a victim can grasp you during a rescue.
   d. Use a rescue tube only when the victim is heavier than you are.

2. **The swimming extension rescue, the active victim rear rescue, and the passive victim rear rescue are all rescue skills used for—**
   a. Multiple victims.
   b. Victims at or near the surface.
   c. Submerged victims.
   d. Spinal injury victims.

3. **Sometimes a victim is unconscious or too exhausted to climb out of the pool. You may have to remove the victim from the water. Make this decision based on which of the following?**
   a. The victim's condition
   b. How long it may be before emergency personnel arrive
   c. The size of the victim
   d. The help available to assist you
   e. If you are at the end of your lifeguarding shift

4. **Follow-up care may include which of the following?**
   a. CPR
   b. Rescue breathing
   c. First aid to control bleeding
   d. Blankets or dry towels to keep the victim warm
   e. Keeping the victim calm

Circle True or False.

5. **Do the stride jump entry with a rescue tube only from a height greater than 3 feet.**

   True   False

6. **Use the compact jump to jump from the deck into water that is less than 5 feet deep.**

   True   False

7. **You can use the same skill to rescue a submerged victim regardless of whether the victim is active or passive.**

   True   False

8. **Put the steps for the general procedure for a water emergency in the right order (Number 1-6):**
   ____ Determine if the victim is distressed, active, or passive.
   ____ Move the victim to safety.
   ____ Give emergency care as needed.
   ____ Survey the scene and safely enter the water.
   ____ Remove the victim from the water.
   ____ Perform an appropriate rescue.

chapter 6

breathing
and cardiac emergencies

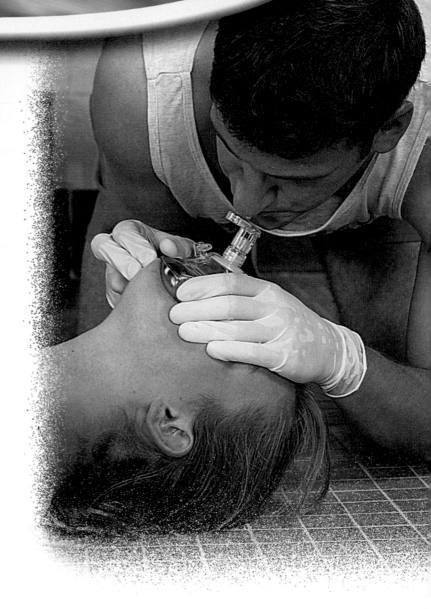

As a lifeguard, you are a professional rescuer. That makes you a key part of the emergency medical services (EMS) system. While on duty, you are legally obligated, within the bounds of your training, to respond and give care in an emergency. As a lifeguard and professional rescuer, you must be able to—

- *Respond in an emergency.*
- *Ensure personal and bystander safety.*
- *Gain access to the victim.*
- *Get consent when providing care.*
- *Determine whether any life-threatening conditions are present.*
- *Provide needed care for the victim.*
- *Summon more help when needed.*
- *Use techniques learned in your training.*

Before Providing Care

Obtaining Consent

Before giving care to a conscious victim, you must first have his or her consent. To get consent—

- State your name.
- Tell the victim you are trained to help.
- Ask the victim if you can help.
- Explain what you think may be wrong.
- Explain what you plan to do.

When the victim gives consent, give care. If the victim does not give consent, do not give care, but call 9-1-1 or the local emergency number. A victim who is unconscious, confused, or seriously ill may not be able to give consent. Then consent is implied. This means that the victim would agree to the care if he or she could, so you should give care.

Lifeguarding Tip: Remember to document any refusal of care by the victim(s).

Basic Precautions to Prevent Disease Transmission

The risk of getting a disease from giving first aid or CPR is very low. Follow these basic precautions to reduce the risk:

- Avoid contact with blood and other body fluids.
- Use protective equipment, such as disposable gloves, breathing barriers, and footwear.
- Carefully wash your hands with soap and water immediately after giving care.

For more information on preventing disease transmission, the American Red Cross Lifeguarding program includes additional optional training in preventing disease transmission (Blood Borne Pathogens).

Breathing Barriers

Breathing barriers include resuscitation masks, face shields, and bag-valve-mask resuscitators (BVMs). Breathing barriers help protect you against disease transmission when giving rescue breaths to a victim. The breathing barriers discussed in the American Red Cross Lifeguard Training course are resuscitation masks and BVMs.

Resuscitation Masks

Resuscitation masks are flexible devices that fit over the victim's nose and mouth so that you can breathe air into the victim's lungs without making mouth-to-mouth contact (Fig. 6-1). The facility usually provides resuscitation masks for lifeguards to use. Be sure the mask you use has the following characteristics, or ask management for a different one:

- Is easy to assemble and use
- Has a one-way valve for releasing exhaled air
- Works well in all of conditions
- Has a standard (transferable) connecting assembly
- Has an inlet for supplemental oxygen delivery

Bag-Valve-Mask Resuscitators

A bag-valve-mask (BVM) resuscitator is a hand-held device used to get oxygen into a nonbreathing victim (Fig. 6-2). It can also be used for a victim in respiratory distress. Because it is necessary to maintain a tight seal on the mask, you need two rescuers to operate the BVM (one rescuer positions and seals the mask, while the second rescuer squeezes the bag). The BVM—

Fig. 6-1

Fig. 6-2

- Protects you against disease transmission.
- Increases oxygen levels in the blood.
- Is highly effective when used by two rescuers.

General Procedures for Cleaning Up a Blood Spill

If a victim's blood is spilled on the floor or other surface—

- Clean up the spill immediately or as soon as possible.
- Wear disposable gloves and other protective equipment, such as footwear, masks and shields, and protective eyewear when cleaning spills.
- Wipe up the spill with paper towels or other absorbent material.
- After the spill has been wiped up, flood the area with a solution of $1/4$ cup of liquid chlorine bleach to 1 gallon of fresh water, and allow it to stand for at least 20 minutes.
- Dispose of the contaminated material used to clean up the spill in a labeled biohazard container.

Preventing Disease Transmission Quiz

Directions: Read each question and circle whether it is True or False.

1. True False Do not touch your mouth, nose, or eyes when giving care.

2. True False Avoid letting objects that may have been in contact with blood or other bodily fluids touch your skin.

3. True False Cover any cuts, scrapes, or skin irritations prior to using protective equipment.

4. True False Use disposable gloves only if you suspect the victim has a disease.

5. True False Avoid contact with broken glass, needles, or other sharp objects.

6. True False If you come in direct contact with a victim's body fluids while giving care, do not tell anybody, especially your supervisor or doctor.

7. True False Remove jewelry from your hands before putting on disposable gloves.

General Procedures for Injury or Sudden Illness on Land

When someone suddenly becomes ill or injured, activate the facility's emergency action plan (EAP). Use first aid equipment and supplies and follow these general procedures:

- **Survey the scene and approach the victim.** Determine whether the scene is safe, what happened, how many victims are involved, and if any bystanders can help.
- **Do a primary survey.** Check for conditions that are an immediate threat to a victim's life. You identify signs of life-threatening conditions and care for them. When performing a primary survey—
  - Use basic precautions to prevent disease transmission (disposable gloves and breathing barriers).
  - Get consent (when possible).
  - Check the victim for consciousness.
  - Check the ABCs (airway, breathing, and circulation).
  - Check for severe bleeding.

Also, ask yourself these questions:

- Is the victim conscious?
- Is the airway open?
- Is the victim breathing?
- Does the victim show signs of circulation? Signs of circulation include normal breathing, coughing or movement in response to rescue breaths, and pulse.
- Is there severe bleeding?

- **Call 9-1-1 or the local emergency number.** Call, or have someone call, EMS if any of the following conditions exist:
  - Unconsciousness or disorientation
  - Breathing problems (difficulty breathing or no breathing)
  - Chest pain or discomfort lasting more than 3-5 minutes
  - Shows no signs of circulation
  - Severe bleeding
  - Suspected head, neck, or back injuries
  - Severe headache or slurred speech
  - Seizures that occur in the water, seizures that last more than 5 minutes, repeated seizures (one after another), the seizure victim is pregnant, or the victim does not regain consciousness after a seizure
  - Vomiting or urinating blood
  - Suspected poisoning

- **Do a secondary survey.** Perform a secondary survey to identify and care for additional conditions. Do a secondary survey only if you are sure that the victim does not have any life-threatening conditions. The secondary survey is a method of gathering additional information about injuries or conditions that may need care. These injuries or conditions may not be life-threatening but could become so if not cared for.

The secondary survey includes the following steps:

1. Follow basic precautions to prevent disease transmission (disposable gloves and breathing barriers).

2. Interview the victim and bystanders. If you have not already done so, get consent from a victim (parents/guardian if the victim is a minor) before helping. Ask the following questions:

   - Do you feel any pain anywhere?
   - Do you have any medical conditions or take medication?
   - Do you have any allergies?
   - When did you last eat or drink anything?

3. Do a visual head-to-toe examination.

- Begin at the top of the head, face, ears, nose, and mouth.
- Look at the coloring of the victim's face and lips.
- Look at the skin.
- Look over the body.
- Watch for changes in consciousness and breathing.
- After you have completed the secondary survey, care for any condition you have found (if any) and have the victim rest comfortably.
- Note the information you find in the secondary survey. If 9-1-1 or the local emergency number has been called, give this information to EMS personnel when they arrive and take over.

Lifeguarding Tip: If any life-threatening conditions develop when you perform the secondary survey, stop whatever you are doing and provide care immediately.

If You Are The Only Rescuer

If you are the only trained rescuer at a facility when an emergency occurs, you should **Call First** *or* **Call Fast.** *Calling First or Calling Fast means that the rescuer may have to balance between calling EMS immediately or providing initial care for approximately one minute, and then calling EMS, if he or she is alone. Whenever there is another rescuer or bystander available, the rescuer should always direct that person to call EMS as soon as it is determined that a victim is unconscious or another life-threatening condition is discovered, while the rescuer continues to give care.*

Call First

Call 9-1-1 or the local emergency number **First** before providing care for an unconscious adult victim and an unconscious infant or child known to be at high risk for heart problems.

Call Fast

Give one minute of care, then call 9-1-1 or the local emergency number **Fast** for:

- An unconscious child or infant.
- A submersion or near drowning.
- An arrest associated with trauma.
- Drug overdoses.

Moving a Victim

When a victim is injured out of the water, in many cases, you will care for the victim where you find him or her. If the victim's injury is minor, he or she will probably be able to go to the first aid station. Moving a victim needlessly can lead to further injury. Move an injured victim only if—

- The scene is becoming unsafe. (For example, fire, risk of explosion, a hazardous chemical leak, or a collapsing structure)
- You have to reach another victim who may have a more serious injury or illness.
- You need to provide proper care. (For example, someone has collapsed on a stairway, does not show signs of circulation, and needs CPR. CPR needs to be performed on a firm, flat surface.)

Clothes Drag

To move a clothed victim who you think may have a head, neck, or back injury—

1. Gather the victim's clothing behind the victim's neck (Fig. 6-3).
2. Pull the victim to safety.
3. While moving the victim, cradle the head with the victim's clothes and your hands.

Two-Person Seat Carry

To carry a conscious victim who cannot walk and has no suspected head, neck, or back injury, enlist the help of another lifeguard or a bystander and—

1. Put one arm under the victim's thighs and the other across the victim's back.

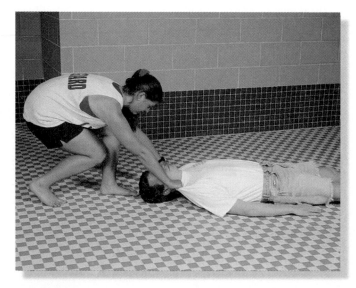

Fig. 6-3

2. Interlock your arms with those of a second rescuer under the victim's legs and across the victim's back (Fig. 6-4A-B).

3. Move the victim to safety (Fig. 6-4C)

Fig. 6-4A

Fig. 6-4B

Fig. 6-4C

Walking Assist

To help a victim who needs assistance walking to safety—

1. Place the victim's arm across your shoulders, and hold it in place with one hand.

2. Support the victim with your other hand around the victim's waist (Fig. 6-5).

3. Move the victim to safety.

Fig. 6-5

Blanket Drag

To move an unconscious victim in an emergency situation when equipment is limited—

1. Keep the victim between you and the blanket.

2. Gather half the blanket and place it against the victim's side.

3. Roll the victim as a unit toward you.

4. Reach over and place the blanket so that it will be positioned under the victim.

5. Roll the victim onto the blanket.

6. Gather the blanket at the head and drag the victim (Fig. 6-6).

Fig. 6-6

Foot Drag

To move a victim too large to carry or move otherwise—

1. Firmly grasp the victim's ankles and move backwards (Fig. 6-7).

2. Pull the victim in a straight line, and be careful not to bump the victim's head.

Fig. 6-7

Breathing Emergencies

You may detect a breathing emergency during the primary survey. A breathing emergency occurs if a victim has difficulty breathing or stops breathing. For example, a drowning victim you rescued may not be breathing, or a swimmer on deck may have difficulty breathing due to an asthma attack. Breathing emergencies can be caused by—

- Near drowning.
- Obstructed airway (choking).
- Respiratory distress or illness (emphysema, asthma, anaphylactic shock, hyperventilation, pneumonia).
- Electrocution.
- Shock.
- Heart attack.
- Coronary heart disease.
- Injury to the chest and lungs.
- Allergic reactions (food or insect stings).
- Poisoning.
- Drugs.

Respiratory Distress

A victim who is having difficulty breathing is in respiratory distress. Signs and symptoms of respiratory distress include—

- Slow or rapid breathing.
- Shortness of breath.
- Dizziness or lightheadedness.
- Tingling in hands or feet.
- Chest pain or discomfort.
- Skin flushed, pale, ashen, or bluish.
- Gasping for breath.
- Wheezing, gurgling, or making high-pitched noises.

Caring for Respiratory Distress

You do not need to know the cause of respiratory distress to provide care. Whenever you find a victim experiencing difficulty breathing—

- Call 9-1-1 or the local emergency number.
- Use basic precautions to prevent disease transmission.
- Help the victim rest in a comfortable position.
- Reassure and comfort the victim.
- Help the victim with any prescribed medication.
- Keep the victim from getting chilled or overheated.
- Give supplemental oxygen if it is available and if you are trained to do so.

Respiratory Arrest

A victim who has stopped breathing is in respiratory arrest. The victim gets no oxygen. The body can function only for 4-6 minutes without oxygen before serious brain damage begins. The heart soon stops. Not long after the heart stops, permanent disability or death may occur.

Rescue Breathing

Rescue breathing is a technique for breathing air into a victim to give him or her the oxygen needed to survive. The air you breathe out contains enough oxygen to keep a victim alive. Whenever possible, use a resuscitation mask when giving rescue breathing.

Check the victim for breathing during the primary survey. If you cannot see, hear, or feel signs of breathing in an adult (ages 9 and up), child (ages 1 to 8), or infant (up to 1 year of age), begin rescue breathing. Continue rescue breathing until—

- The victim begins to breathe on his or her own.
- Another trained rescuer takes over for you.
- You are too exhausted to continue.
- The victim shows no signs of circulation (begin CPR).
- The scene becomes unsafe.

Rescue Breathing-Special Situations

Air in the Stomach

When giving rescue breathing, breathe slowly, just enough to make the victim's chest clearly rise. If you blow in too much air, it will enter the stomach. Then the victim will likely vomit. Vomit into the airway that gets into the lungs can cause an obstruction.

Vomiting and Drowning

When you give rescue breathing to a near-drowning victim, the victim will likely vomit. Quickly turn the victim on his or her side. Support the head and neck and turn the body away from you as one unit. Turning the victim onto his or her side keeps vomit from blocking the airway and entering the lungs. Quickly wipe the victim's mouth clean (or suction the mouth clean if you have the equipment and are trained to do so). Then turn the victim on his or her back, and continue with rescue breathing.

Mask-to-Nose Breathing

If the victim's mouth is injured, you may need to give rescue breathing through the nose. Perform mask-to-nose breathing this way:

1. Use a resuscitation mask.

2. Maintain the head-tilt position.

3. Place the resuscitation mask over the victim's nose and mouth.

4. Use both hands to close the victim's mouth by pulling up on the chin.

5. Seal the resuscitation mask with both hands, and then give breaths.

Mask-to-Stoma Breathing

Some people have had an operation that removed part of their windpipe. They breathe through an opening in the front of their neck called a stoma. If you see a stoma in someone you are about to give rescue breathing to, follow the same steps for mouth-to-mask breathing, except—

- Look, listen, and feel for breathing with the ear over the stoma.

- Maintain the airway in a neutral position (the stoma provides access to the lower airway).

- Use a child or infant resuscitation mask over the victim's stoma.

- Use both hands to seal the resuscitation mask over the stoma to give breaths.

Victims with Dentures

If the victim is wearing dentures, leave them in place unless they become loose and block the airway.

Suspected Head, Neck, or Back Injuries

If you think the victim has a head, neck, or back injury, try to open the airway by lifting the chin without tilting the head. Use the two-handed jaw thrust technique (Fig. 6-8):

1. Place a resuscitation mask over the victim's mouth.

2. Place your fingers under the angles of the victim's jaw and lift.

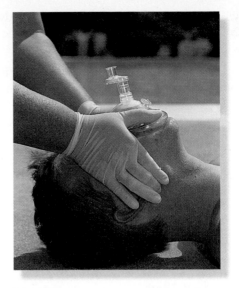

Fig. 6-8

3. Without moving the victim's head, seal the mask and then breathe into the victim.

Airway Obstruction

Choking is the most common cause of respiratory emergencies. A victim who is clutching his or her throat with one or both hands is usually choking. In an unconscious victim, the tongue often blocks the airway and causes a respiratory emergency.

Causes of choking include—

- Poorly chewed food.

- Drinking alcohol before or during meals. Alcohol dulls the nerves that aid swallowing, making choking on food more likely.

- Eating too fast or talking or laughing while eating.

- Walking, playing, or running with food or objects in the mouth.

Lifeguards must be able to recognize when a victim is choking. The airway may be partially or completely obstructed. Victims with a partial airway obstruction make wheezing sounds and can still move some air to and from the lungs. Victims with a complete airway obstruction cannot speak, breathe, or cough effectively. Get consent before helping a conscious choking victim. If the choking victim is unconscious, consent is implied.

Cardiac Emergencies

Cardiac Chain of Survival

The EMS system functions as a cardiac chain of survival. In a cardiac emergency every second counts. Follow the four links in the cardiac chain of survival:

1. **Early recognition of the emergency and early access to EMS.** The sooner 9-1-1 or local emergency number is called, the sooner EMS arrives and takes over.

2. **Early cardiopulmonary resuscitation (CPR)** helps supply oxygen to the brain and other vital organs to keep the victim alive until an automated external defibrillator (AED) is used or advanced life support arrives.

3. **Early defibrillation:** An electric shock called defibrillation may restore a normal heart beat. Each minute defibrillation is delayed reduces the victim's chance of survival by 10 percent.

4. **Early advanced life support** is given by EMS personnel who provide further care and transport to the hospital.

Recognizing a Heart Attack

The sooner you recognize a heart attack and act, the better chance you have to save a life. Call 9-1-1 or your local emergency number if the victim has these signs and symptoms:

- Chest pain or discomfort lasting more than 3-5 minutes.
- Pain, discomfort, or pressure in either arm that spreads to the shoulder, arm, jaw, or back.
- Nausea, shortness of breath, or difficulty breathing.
- Sweating or changes in skin appearance.
- Dizziness or unconsciousness.

Care for a Heart Attack

If you think someone is having a heart attack—

- Call 9-1-1 or the local emergency number.
- Have the victim stop what he or she is doing and rest (the victim is likely to deny the possibility of having a heart attack).
- Have the victim sit in any position in which breathing is easiest.
- Be calm and reassuring.
- Do a secondary survey.
- Help the victim take only prescribed medication and give oxygen (if it is available and you are trained to do so).
- Monitor the victim for signs of circulation and breathing.
- Give CPR if the victim loses consciousness and shows no signs of circulation.

Cardiac Arrest

Cardiac arrest occurs when the heart stops beating or beats too irregularly or too weakly to circulate blood effectively. Cardiac arrest is a life-threatening emergency. Serious brain damage can begin within 4-6 minutes. Signals of cardiac arrest include—

- No signs of circulation.
- No breathing.
- Unconsciousness.

Cardiac arrest can occur suddenly and without warning. Other times, victims experience signs and symptoms of a heart attack before the cardiac arrest.

CPR

A victim who shows no signs of circulation needs cardiopulmonary resuscitation (CPR). CPR combines rescue breaths and chest compressions. Chest compressions help to circulate blood in the victim's body after the heart stops. Together, rescue breaths and chest compressions increase a cardiac arrest victim's chances of survival by getting oxygen to the brain and other vital organs. Without CPR, the brain will suffer damage within 4 to 6 minutes! Calling 9-1-1 or the local emergency number immediately is critical for the victim's survival. If the cardiac arrest occurs in the water, first immediately remove the victim from the water. Place him or her on the deck or shoreline, and give CPR. If you are trained in the use of an automated external defibrillator (AED), use it with CPR until EMS arrives and takes over.

Infant and Child CPR

CPR for infants and children is similar to the technique for adults, but you modify it for smaller body sizes and faster breathing and heart rates. Cardiac arrest in infants and children usually is caused by a respiratory emergency. If you recognize an infant or child in respiratory distress or arrest, give care immediately. If cardiac arrest occurs, begin CPR.

Two-Rescuer CPR

Two-rescuer CPR is easier and more effective than giving CPR by yourself. Perform two-rescuer CPR whenever another trained rescuer is on the scene with you, even if you had already started CPR by yourself.

CPR-Special Situations

You may have to move a victim to give CPR in difficult locations:

- Move a victim from a cramped or busy location only if it is unsafe or impractical to perform CPR there.
- In a stairwell, move the victim to a flat area at the head or foot of the stairs to perform CPR. Never interrupt CPR longer than about 30 seconds.

Oxygen Administration

If you may be caring for near drowning, breathing, and cardiac emergencies, you would benefit from training in oxygen administration. Giving supplemental oxygen helps meet the injured or ill victim's increased need for oxygen. Supplemental oxygen provides higher oxygen concentration for the victim. The American Red Cross Lifeguarding program includes optional training in the use of supplemental oxygen.

Automated External Defibrillators (AEDs)

Automated external defibrillators are critical for the survival of many cardiac arrest victims. AEDs are available in many public places, including pools, waterfronts, and waterparks. AED training is an important skill for lifeguards. Always promptly start and continue CPR until a defibrillator is brought to the scene. The American Red Cross Lifeguarding program includes optional training in the use of AEDs.

Putting it All Together

As a professional rescuer, you are an important part of the EMS system. You have a duty to act and to meet professional standards. Follow the general procedures for an injured or ill victim on land: survey the scene, do a primary survey, call 9-1-1 or the local emergency number, and, after caring for any life-threatening injuries, do a secondary survey. Use basic precautions to protect yourself against disease transmission. Recognizing and caring for breathing and cardiac emergencies are among the most important lifeguard skills you'll learn.

in review...

Circle the best answer or answers.

1. **To give care for an ill or injured person, you must first—**
   a. Obtain the person's consent.
   b. Begin to write your record of what happened.
   c. Ask bystanders what happened.
   d. Find out if you have a duty to act.

2. **Basic precautions to prevent disease transmission include—**
   a. Avoiding contact with blood and other body fluids.
   b. Calling 9-1-1 immediately.
   c. Using protective equipment.
   d. Carefully washing hands with soap and water after giving care.

3. **General procedures for injury or sudden illness on land include—**
   a. Surveying the scene and approaching the victim.
   b. Planning for when an emergency occurs.
   c. Performing the primary and secondary survey.
   d. Calling 9-1-1 or the local emergency number.

4. **Why should you do a primary survey in every situation?**
   a. To protect you from legal liability
   b. To identify any immediate threat to the victim's life
   c. To protect the victim and bystanders from dangers at the scene
   d. To reassure the victim

5. **The purpose of the secondary survey is to—**
   a. Identify and care for additional problems that are not life threatening.
   b. Determine if the victim is bleeding severely.
   c. Look for other victims you may not have noticed at first.
   d. Find out if the victim has medical insurance.

6. **When you give rescue breathing to a victim, you are—**
   a. Artificially circulating oxygenated blood to the body cells.
   b. Supplementing the air the victim is already breathing.
   c. Giving the victim oxygen necessary for survival.
   d. Giving the victim enough air to stay conscious.

7. **Breathing barriers help—**
   a. Protect against disease transmission.
   b. Perform CPR.
   c. Maintain breathing.
   d. Reduce the amount of oxygen in a victim's blood.

8. **Links in the cardiac chain of survival include—**
   a. Early rescue breathing.
   b. Early recognition of the emergency and early access to EMS.
   c. Early defibrillation.
   d. Early advanced life support.
   e. Early CPR.
   f. Early recognition of a safe scene.

in review...

9. **You find a 6-year-old boy unconscious for an unknown cause. You do the primary survey and find that the boy is not breathing but shows signs of circulation. How often do you need to breathe for this victim?**

   a. Once every 3 seconds.

   b. Once every 5 seconds.

   c. Once every minute.

   d. Twelve times a minute.

10. **You just saw an older man collapse on the pool deck. You do the primary survey and find the man is not breathing and does not have a pulse. You begin CPR. How many chest compressions and rescue breaths do you give in each cycle?**

    a. 12 chest compressions and 1 rescue breath

    b. 12 chest compressions and 2 rescue breaths

    c. 15 chest compressions and 1 rescue breath

    d. 15 chest compressions and 2 rescue breaths

    e. 5 chest compressions and 1 rescue breath

    f. 5 chest compressions and 2 rescue breaths

primary survey

Remember: Always follow basic precautions to prevent disease transmission. Use protective equipment (disposable gloves and breathing barriers). Wash your hands immediately after giving care.

1. Survey the scene for safety, then check the victim for consciousness.

2. Tap the victim's shoulder and shout to see if the victim responds.

   For an infant, gently tap the infant's shoulder or foot.

3. *If the victim does not respond—*
   Have someone else call 9-1-1 or the local emergency number.

4. Without moving the victim, look, listen, and feel for breathing for about 5 seconds.

5. *If the victim is not breathing or you cannot tell—*
   Roll the victim onto the back, while supporting the head and neck.

6. Tilt the head back and lift the chin to open the airway. Look, listen, and feel for breathing for about 5 seconds.

Lifeguarding Tip: Do not tilt a child's or infant's head back as far as an adult's head.

7. *If the victim is not breathing—*
   Give 2 rescue breaths.

   - Assemble and position the resuscitation mask.

   - Tilt the head back and lift the chin to open the airway.

   - Take a breath before you give each rescue breath.

   - Give breaths that will make the chest clearly rise.

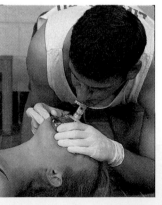

Lifeguarding Tip: Use a smaller resuscitation mask for a child or infant, if available. If an infant resuscitation mask is not available, use the adult mask by turning the mask so that the nose end of it is on the infant's chin.

If breaths do not go in, go to:

- Unconscious Choking—Adult and Child Skill Sheet, pages 68-69.
- Unconscious Choking—Infant Skill Sheet, pages 70-71.

8. If breaths go in—
   Check the victim for signs of circulation.

- Remove the resuscitation mask.
- **Adult and Child:** Find the Adam's apple and slide your fingers toward you and down into the groove at the side of the neck.

- **Infant:** Find the brachial pulse on the inside of the upper arm, between the infant's elbow and shoulder.

- Look, listen, and feel for signs of circulation for no more than 10 seconds.
- Look for severe bleeding.

If there are signs of circulation and breathing—

Place the victim in a recovery position (adult or child only) and continue to monitor for signs of circulation and breathing.

If there are signs of circulation and NO breathing—

Give rescue breathing.

- Rescue Breathing—Adult Skill Sheet, page 64
- Rescue Breathing—Child Skill Sheet, page 65
- Rescue Breathing—Infant Skill Sheet, page 66

If there are NO signs of circulation—

Perform CPR.

- CPR—Adult Skill Sheet, pages 72-73
- CPR—Child Skill Sheet, pages 74-75
- CPR—Infant Skill Sheet, pages 76-77

rescue breathing—adult

Complete Steps 1-8, Primary Survey Skill Sheet, pages 62-63

Remember: Always follow basic precautions to prevent disease transmission.

9. If there are signs of circulation but no breathing—
    Give 1 rescue breath.

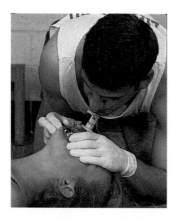

- Tilt the head back and lift the chin to open the airway.
- Position the resuscitation mask.
- Take a breath before you give a rescue breath.
- Give a breath that will make the chest clearly rise.
- Each rescue breath should last about 2 seconds.

10. Continue to give 1 rescue breath about every 5 seconds.

- Do this for about 1 minute (12 breaths).
- Watch the chest clearly rise and fall when giving each breath.

11. Recheck signs of circulation and breathing for no more than 10 seconds

- Remove the resuscitation mask.

Lifeguarding Tip: Always recheck signs of circulation and breathing about every minute when giving rescue breathing.

12. If there are signs of circulation and still no breathing—
    Continue rescue breathing.

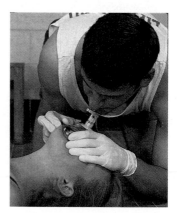

- Replace the resuscitation mask.

If there are signs of circulation and breathing—

Place the victim in the recovery position and monitor for signs of circulation and breathing.

If there are NO signs of circulation—

Perform CPR.

- CPR—Adult Skill Sheet, pages 72-73

rescue breathing–child

Complete Steps 1-8, Primary Survey Skill Sheet, pages 62-63

Remember: Always follow basic precautions to prevent disease transmission.

9. If there are signs of circulation but no breathing—
   Give rescue breaths.

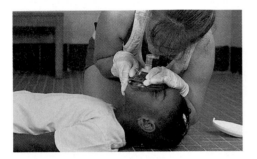

- Tilt the head back and lift the chin to open the airway.
- Position the resuscitation mask.
- Take a breath before you give a rescue breath.
- Give a breath that will make the chest clearly rise.
- Each rescue breath should last about $1^1/2$ seconds.

10. Continue to give 1 rescue breath about every 3 seconds.

- Do this for about 1 minute (20 breaths).
- Watch the chest clearly rise and fall when giving each breath.

11. Recheck for signs of circulation and breathing for no more than 10 seconds.

- Remove the resuscitation mask.

Lifeguarding Tip: Always recheck signs of circulation and breathing about every minute when giving rescue breathing.

12. If there are signs of circulation and still no breathing—
   Continue rescue breathing.

- Replace the resuscitation mask.

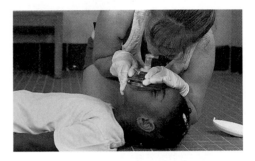

If there are signs of circulation and breathing—

Place the child in the recovery position and continue to monitor the child for signs of circulation and breathing.

If there are NO signs of circulation—

Perform CPR.

- CPR—Child Skill Sheet, pages 74-75

rescue breathing–infant

Complete Steps 1-8, Primary Survey Skill Sheet, pages 62-63
Remember: Always follow basic precautions to prevent disease transmission.

9. If there are signs of circulation but no breathing—
   Give rescue breaths.

   ■ Tilt the head back and lift the chin to open the airway.
   ■ Position the resuscitation mask.
   ■ Take a breath before you give a rescue breath.
   ■ Give a breath that will make the chest clearly rise.
   ■ Each rescue breath should last about $1^1/_2$ seconds.

10. Continue to give 1 rescue breath about every 3 seconds.

   ■ Do this for about 1 minute (20 breaths).
   ■ Watch the chest clearly rise and fall when giving each breath.

11. Recheck for signs of circulation and breathing for no more than 10 seconds.

   ■ Remove the resuscitation mask.

Lifeguarding Tip: Always recheck signs of circulation and breathing about every minute when giving rescue breathing.

12. If there are signs of circulation and still no breathing—
   Continue rescue breathing.

   ■ Replace the resuscitation mask.

If there are signs of circulation and breathing—

Continue to monitor the infant for signs of circulation and breathing.

If there are NO signs of circulation—

Perform CPR.

   ■ CPR—Infant Skill Sheet, pages 76-77

conscious choking—
adult and child

Remember: Always follow basic precautions to prevent disease transmission.

1. Survey the scene and then check the victim.
   - Ask the victim if he or she is choking.
   - Identify yourself and ask if you can help.

Remember: Be sure to get permission before caring for a conscious child. Tell the child's parent or guardian your level of training and the care you are going to provide.

   - If the victim is coughing forcefully, encourage continued coughing.

2. If the victim cannot cough, speak, or breathe— Have someone else call 9-1-1 or the local emergency number.

3. Give abdominal thrusts.
   - **Adult:** Stand behind the victim, placing one foot between the victim's legs.
   - **Child:** Stand or kneel behind the child depending on the child's size.
   - Place the thumb side of your fist against the middle of the victim's abdomen, just above the navel.

   - Grab your fist with your other hand.
   - Give quick, upward thrusts.

Note: *Some choking victims require chest thrusts instead of abdominal thrusts.*
Use chest thrusts if—

   - *You cannot reach far enough around the victim to give abdominal thrusts.*
   - *The victim is pregnant.*

To perform chest thrusts—

1. *Stand behind the victim.*
2. *Make a fist with one hand and place the thumb side against the center of the victim's breastbone.*
3. *Grab your fist with your other hand and give quick, inward thrusts.*
4. *Repeat the thrusts until the object is expelled.*

4. Continue giving abdominal thrusts until—
   - The object is forced out.
   - The victim begins to breathe or cough forcefully on his or her own.
   - The victim becomes unconscious.
   - If the victim becomes unconscious, go to: Unconscious Choking—Adult and Child Skill Sheet, pages 68-69.

unconscious choking— adult and child

Complete Steps 1-7, Primary Survey Skill Sheet, pages 62-63.

Remember: Always follow basic precautions to prevent disease transmission.

8. If breaths do not go in—
   Reposition the airway by tilting the head further back and give 2 rescue breaths again.

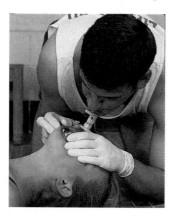

9. If breaths still do not go in—
   Give up to 5 abdominal thrusts.

   - Remove the resuscitation mask.
   - Straddle one or both of the victim's legs.
   - Place the heel of one hand against the middle of the victim's abdomen, just above the navel.
   - Place your other hand on top with your fingers pointing toward the victim's head.

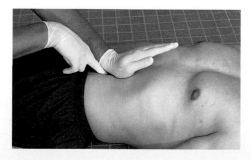

- Press into the abdomen with upward thrusts.

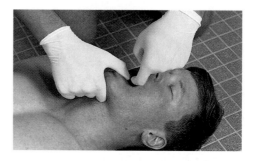

10. Foreign object check.

    Adult

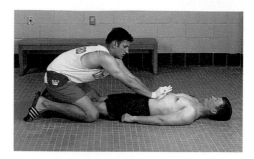

- Grasp the tongue and lower jaw between your thumb and fingers and lift the jaw.
- Slide your index finger along the inside of the cheek using a hooking motion to sweep the object out.

Child

- Grasp the tongue and lower jaw between your thumb and fingers and lift the jaw.
- Look for a foreign object.
- If you see something, sweep it out with your little finger.

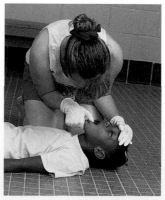

11. Give 2 rescue breaths.

- Replace the resuscitation mask.

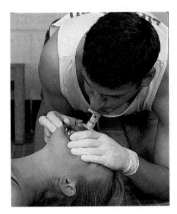

12. If the breaths still do not go in—
Repeat Steps 8-11.

If the breaths go in—
Check for signs of circulation and breathing for no more than 10 seconds.

If there are signs of circulation and breathing—

Place the victim in a recovery position and continue to monitor for signs of circulation and breathing.

If there are signs of circulation and NO breathing—

Give rescue breathing.

- Rescue Breathing—Adult Skill Sheet, page 64
- Rescue Breathing—Child Skill Sheet, page 65
- Rescue Breathing—Infant Skill Sheet, page 66

If there are NO signs of circulation—

Perform CPR.

- CPR—Adult Skill Sheet, pages 72-73
- CPR—Child Skill Sheet, pages 74-75

unconscious choking—infant

Complete Steps 1-7, Primary Survey Skill Sheet, pages 62-63

Remember: Always follow basic precautions to prevent disease transmission.

8. If breaths do not go in—
   Reposition the airway by tilting the head further back and give 2 rescue breaths again.

9. If breaths still do not go in—
   Give 5 back blows and 5 chest thrusts.

   - Remove the resuscitation mask.
   - Carefully position the infant facedown along your forearm, with your hand supporting the infant's head and neck.
   - Keep the infant's head lower than his or her chest.
   - With the heel of your other hand, strike the infant between the shoulder blades 5 times.

- Turn the infant over, and place two fingers in the center of the breastbone.
- Give 5 chest thrusts. Each thrust should be about $1/2$ to 1 inch deep.

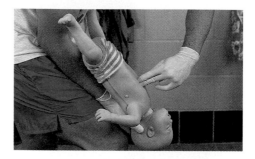

10. Look for a foreign object.

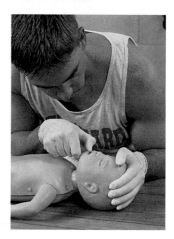

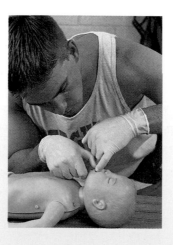

- Grasp the tongue and lower jaw between your thumb and fingers and lift the jaw.
- If an object is seen, sweep it out with your little finger.

11. Give 2 rescue breaths.

- Replace the resuscitation mask.

12. If the breaths still do not go in—
Check for signs of circulation and breathing for no more than 10 seconds.

If there are signs of circulation and breathing—

Continue to monitor the infant for signs of circulation and breathing.

If there are signs of circulation and NO breathing—

Give rescue breathing.

- Rescue Breathing—Infant Skill Sheet, page 66

If there are NO signs of circulation—

Perform CPR.

- CPR—Infant Skill Sheet, pages 76-77

CPR—adult

Complete Steps 1-8, Primary Survey Skill Sheet, pages 62-63

Remember: Always follow basic precautions to prevent disease transmission.

9. If the victim shows no signs of circulation— Find hand position on the breastbone.

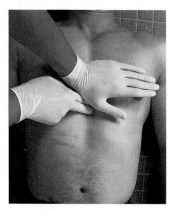

- Find the notch at the lower end of the victim's breastbone by sliding your middle and index fingers up the edge of the ribcage where the ribs meet the breastbone.
- Place the heel of one hand next to and above the notch.
- Place your hand on top of the other.

10. Give 15 chest compressions.

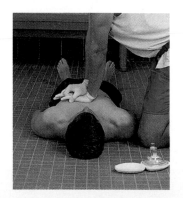

- Position the shoulders over the hands with the elbows locked.
- Compress the chest about 2 inches at a rate of about 100 compressions per minute.

Lifeguarding Tips:

- *Use your body weight, not your arms, to compress the chest.*
- *Keep your elbows locked and fingers off the chest when giving compressions.*
- *15 compressions should take about 10 seconds.*

11. Give 2 rescue breaths.

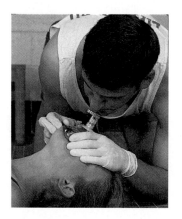

- Replace the resuscitation mask.
- Take a breath before you give each rescue breath.
- Give breaths that will make the chest clearly rise.

12. Do at least 3 more cycles of 15 compressions and 2 rescue breaths.

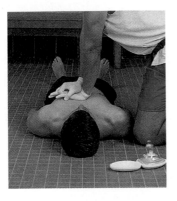

13. Recheck for signs of circulation and breathing for no more than 10 seconds.

- Remove the resuscitation mask.

Lifeguarding Tip: Always recheck signs of circulation every few minutes when giving CPR.

If there are signs of circulation and breathing—

Place the victim in a recovery position and continue to monitor for sings of circulation and breathing.

If there are signs of circulation and NO breathing—

Give rescue breathing.

- Rescue Breathing—Adult Skill Sheet, page 64

If there are still NO signs of circulation—

Continue CPR.

NOTE: Continue CPR until—

- The victim shows signs of circulation.
- Another trained rescuer takes over.
- An AED becomes readily available.
- You are too exhausted to continue.
- The scene becomes unsafe.

CPR–child

Complete Steps 1-8, Primary Survey Skill Sheet, pages 62-63

Remember: Always follow basic precautions to prevent disease transmission.

9. If the child shows no signs of circulation—
Find hand position on the breastbone.

   - Find the notch at the lower end of the child's breastbone by sliding your middle and index fingers up the edge of the ribcage nearest to you where the ribs meet the breastbone.
   - Place your middle finger on the notch.
   - Place the heel of the hand on the center of the breastbone next to where your index finger was.
   - Place your other hand on the child's forehead and tilt the head back to keep the airway open.

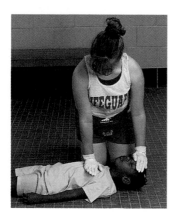

10. Give 5 chest compressions.

    - Position the shoulder over the hand with the elbow locked.
    - Compress the chest about $1^1/_2$ inches at a rate of about 100 compressions per minute.

    Lifeguarding Tips:

    - *Use your body weight, not your arm, to compress the chest.*
    - *Keep your elbow locked and fingers off the chest when giving compressions.*
    - *5 compressions should take about 3 seconds.*

11. Give 1 rescue breath.

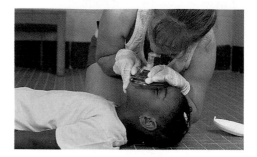

   - Replace the resuscitation mask.
   - Take a breath before you give a rescue breath.
   - Give breaths that will make the chest clearly rise.

12. Do at least 11 more cycles of 5 compressions and 1 rescue breath.

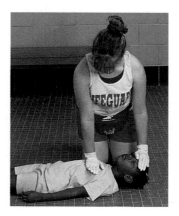

13. Recheck for signs of circulation and breathing for no more than 10 seconds.

Lifeguarding Tip: *Always recheck signs of circulation every few minutes when giving CPR.*

If there are signs of circulation and breathing—

Place the child in the recovery position and continue to monitor for signs of circulation and breathing.

If there are signs of circulation and NO breathing—

Give rescue breathing.

- Rescue Breathing—Child Skill Sheet, page 65

If there are still NO signs of circulation—

Continue CPR.

NOTE: Continue CPR until—

- The child shows signs of circulation.
- Another trained rescuer takes over.
- An AED becomes readily available and is appropriate to use.
- You are too exhausted to continue.
- The scene becomes unsafe.

CPR–infant

Complete Steps 1-8, Primary Survey Skill Sheet, pages 62-63.

Remember: Always follow basic precautions to prevent disease transmission.

Lifeguarding Tip: *Place the infant on his or her back on a firm, flat surface, such as the floor or a table.*

9. If the infant shows no signs of circulation—
   Find finger position on the breastbone.

   - Place your index finger and the pads of the next two fingers on the breastbone just below an imaginary line between the nipples.

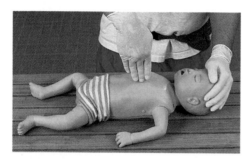

   - Raise your index finger.

   - Place your other hand on the infant's forehead and tilt the head slightly back to keep the airway open.

10. Give 5 chest compressions.

    - Compress the chest about $1/2$ to 1 inch deep at a rate of at least 100 compressions per minute.

Lifeguarding Tip: *5 compressions should take less than 3 seconds.*

11. Give 1 rescue breath.

    - Replace the resuscitation mask.
    - Take a breath before you give a rescue breath.
    - Give breaths that will make the chest clearly rise.

12. Do at least 19 more cycles of 5 chest compressions and 1 rescue breath.

13. Recheck for signs of circulation and breathing for no more than 10 seconds.

If there are signs of circulation and breathing—

Continue to monitor the infant for signs of circulation and breathing.

If there are signs of circulation and NO breathing—

Give rescue breathing.

- Rescue Breathing—Infant Skill Sheet, page 66

If there are still NO signs of circulation—

Continue CPR.

Lifeguarding Tip: *Always recheck signs of circulation every few minutes when giving CPR.*

NOTE: Continue CPR until—

- The infant shows signs of circulation.
- Another trained rescuer takes over.
- You are too exhausted to continue.
- The scene becomes unsafe.

two-rescuer CPR–adult

Rescuer 1 completes Steps 1-8, Primary Survey Skill Sheet, pages 62-63.

Remember: Always follow basic precautions to prevent disease transmission.

9. If the victim shows no signs of circulation— The Rescuer 2 finds hand position on the breastbone.

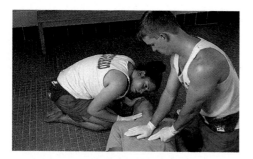

- Find the notch at the lower end of the victim's breastbone by sliding your middle and index fingers up the edge of the ribcage where the ribs meet the breastbone.
- Place the heel of one hand next to and above the notch.
- Place your hand on top of the other.

10. Give 15 compressions.

- Give compressions when Rescuer 1 tells you "Victim has no pulse. Begin CPR."
- Compress the chest about 2 inches at a rate of about 100 compressions per minute.

- Stop compressions and allow the first rescuer to ventilate.

Lifeguarding Tips:

- Use your body weight, not your arms, to compress the chest.
- Keep your elbows locked and fingers off the chest when giving compressions.
- 15 compressions should take about 10 seconds.
- Counting out loud helps keep an even pace and rhythm.
- Rescuer 1 should check effectiveness of compressions by feeling the carotid artery while Rescuer 2 gives compressions.

11. Rescuer 1 gives 2 rescue breaths.
    ■ Position the resuscitation mask.
    ■ Take a breath before you give a rescue breath.
    ■ Give breaths that will make the chest clearly rise.

12. Do at least 3 more cycles of 15 compressions and 2 rescue breaths.

13. Recheck for signs of ciruclation and breathing for no more than 10 seconds.
    ■ Remove the resuscitation mask.

    Lifeguarding Tip: Always recheck signs of circulation every few minutes when giving CPR.

    If there are signs of circulation and breathing—

    Place the victim in the recovery position and monitor for signs of circulation and breathing.

    If there are signs of circulation and NO breathing—

    Give rescue breathing.

    If there are still NO signs of circulation—

    Continue CPR.

14. Changing Positions:
    ■ Rescuer 2 calls for a position change by using the word "change" in place of the word "fifteen" in a compression cycle.
    ■ Rescuer 1 completes 2 rescue breaths.

■ Rescuer 2 moves to the victim's head with his or her own resuscitation mask and checks for signs of circulation and breathing for no more than 10 seconds.
■ Rescuer 1 moves into position at the victim's chest and finds hand position on the victim's breastbone.

■ Rescuer 2 says, "No pulse, continue CPR."
■ Rescuer 1 begins compressions.
■ Continue CPR with cycles of 15 compressions and 2 rescue breaths.

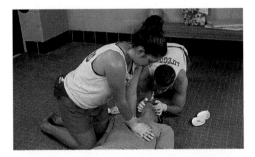

Lifeguarding Tip: Rescuer 2 now rechecks signs of circulation every few minutes when giving CPR and periodically checks effectiveness of compressions by feeling the carotid artery while Rescuer 1 gives compressions.

NOTE: Continue CPR until—

■ The victim shows signs of circulation.
■ Another trained rescuer takes over.
■ An AED becomes readily available.
■ You are too exhausted to continue.
■ The scene becomes unsafe.

using a bag-valve-mask—
two rescuers

Remember: Always follow basic precautions to prevent disease transmission.

1. Rescuer 1 assembles the bag-valve-mask.

   ■ Attach the mask to the bag and valve.

   Lifeguarding Tip: Use smaller bag-valve masks for children and infants.

2. Rescuer 1 positions the mask.

   ■ Place the mask so that it covers the victim's mouth and nose.

3. Rescuer 2 seals the mask and open the airway.

   ■ Place your thumbs on each side of the mask.
   ■ Slide your fingers into position behind the angles of the jawbone.
   ■ Apply downward pressure with your thumbs, lift the jaw, and tilt the head back to open the airway.

4. Rescuer 1 begins ventilations.

   ■ Squeeze the bag slowly for about 2 seconds, using just enough force to make the chest clearly rise.
   ■ Give 1 ventilation about every 5 seconds for an adult and 1 ventilation about every 3 seconds for a child or infant.
   ■ Watch the chest rise and fall with each ventilation.

   Lifeguarding Tip: Always recheck for signs of circulation and breathing about every minute when giving rescue breathing.

chapter 7
first aid

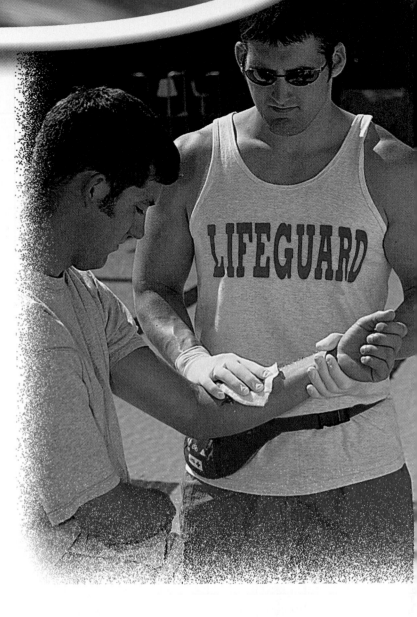

Even when everyone works to prevent emergencies, injuries and illness do occur at aquatic facilities. Every facility needs a first aid area or room where an injured or ill person can be given first aid and can rest. First aid supplies are also kept here (Fig. 7-1). Know where first aid areas are, what first aid equipment and supplies are there, and how to give first aid correctly.

Remember to follow the general procedures for injury or sudden illness on land: survey the scene, do a primary survey, call 9-1-1, and do a secondary survey. Follow basic precautions to prevent disease transmission, such as using disposable gloves and breathing barriers. Carry a few first aid supplies in a fanny pack that you keep with you (Fig. 7-2).

Sudden Illness

Sudden illness can occur to anyone, anywhere. You may not know what the illness is, but you can still give care. Victims of sudden illness usually look and feel ill. If you think something is wrong, check the victim and look for a medical alert tag (Fig. 7-3). The person may try to say nothing is seriously wrong. Do not be afraid to ask the victim questions. The victim's condition can worsen rapidly.

There are many types of sudden illness, such as—

- A diabetic emergency.
- A seizure.
- A stroke.
- An allergic reaction.
- Poisoning.

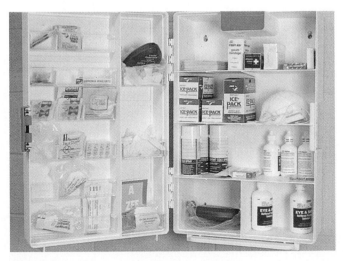

Fig. 7-1

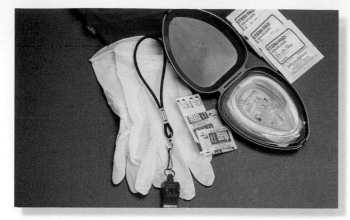

Fig. 7-2

Fig. 7-3

Signs and Symptoms of Sudden Illness

Many different sudden illnesses have similar signs and symptoms. These include—

- Feeling lightheaded, dizzy, or confused.
- Sweating or weakness.
- Changes in skin color (pale, ashen, or flushed).
- Nausea, vomiting, or diarrhea.
- Severe headache, difficulty breathing, or pressure or pain in the chest that won't go away.
- Seizures or changes in consciousness.
- Paralysis, slurred speech, or blurred vision.
- Abdominal pressure or pain that will not go away.

General Care Steps for Sudden Illness

When giving care for sudden illness, follow the general procedures for injury or sudden illness on land and—

- Use basic precautions for preventing disease transmission.
- Care for any life-threatening conditions first.
- Monitor the airway, breathing, and circulation.

- Watch for changes in consciousness.
- Keep the victim comfortable and reassure the victim.
- Keep the victim from getting chilled or overheated.
- Do not give the victim anything to eat or drink unless the victim is fully conscious and is not in shock.
- Care for any other problems that develop, such as vomiting.

Special Situations — Seizures in the Water

If the victim has a seizure in the water—

1. Call or have someone else call 9-1-1 or the local emergency number.

2. Support the victim with the head above water until the seizure ends.

3. Get the victim out of the water as soon as possible (since he or she may have inhaled or swallowed water).

4. Place the victim faceup on the deck and do a primary survey. Give rescue breathing or CPR if needed. If the victim vomits, turn the victim on his or her side to drain fluids from the mouth. Sweep out the mouth (or suction out the mouth if you are trained to do so).

Bites and Stings

Spider Bites/Scorpion Stings

Only two spiders in the United States are poisonous—the black widow and the brown recluse. Their bite can make you very sick or can be fatal. Spider bites usually occur on the hands and arms when people reach into places such as wood, rock, and brush piles or rummage in dark areas.

Some scorpion stings can cause death. If you think someone has been bitten by a black widow or brown recluse or stung by a scorpion—

- Call 9-1-1 or the local emergency number.
- Follow basic precautions for preventing disease transmission.
- Wash the wound.
- Apply a cold pack to the site.
- Care for life-threatening conditions.
- Monitor the airway, breathing, and circulation.
- Keep the victim comfortable.

Snakebites

Snakebites kill very few people in the United States. Of the 8,000 people bitten each year in the United States, less than 12 die. Rattlesnake bites are the most dangerous. To care for someone bitten by a snake—

- Call 9-1-1 or the local emergency number.
- Follow basic precautions for preventing disease transmission.

CARING FOR SUDDEN ILLNESS ACTIVITY

Directions: Match each sudden illness in the first column with the appropriate care steps in the second column. Write the letter of the correct care steps on the line next to the sudden illness.

Stroke _____
- Confusion, dizziness, or disorientation
- Difficulty breathing
- Paralysis to the face, arm, or leg; usually to one side
- Difficulty with speech, vision, or walking
- Severe headache

Seizure _____
- Confusion, dizziness, or disorientation
- Difficulty breathing
- Body may stiffen
- Convulsions followed by—
    - Relaxed state
    - Tired and confused
    - Headache

Diabetic Emergency _____
- Confusion, dizziness, or disorientation
- Difficulty breathing
- Deep, rapid breaths
- Convulsions

Poisoning/Allergic Reaction _____
- Confusion, dizziness, or disorientation
- Difficulty breathing
- Coughing
- Back pain
- Abnormal pulse rate
- Sweating

A
- Call 9-1-1 or the local emergency number and the local poison control center.
- Follow basic precautions for preventing disease transmission.
- Care for life-threatening conditions.
- Monitor the airway, breathing, and circulation.
- Keep the victim comfortable.
- Do not make the victim vomit unless directed to do so.

B
- Call 9-1-1 or the local emergency number.
- Follow basic precautions for preventing disease transmission.
- Care for life-threatening conditions.
- Monitor the airway, breathing, and circulation.
- Keep the victim comfortable.
- If conscious, give the victim some form of sugar.

C
- Call 9-1-1 or the local emergency number.
- Follow basic precautions for preventing disease transmission.
- Care for life-threatening conditions.
- Monitor the airway, breathing, and circulation.
- Keep the victim comfortable.
- Do not give the victim anything to eat or drink.
- Cushion the victim's head.
- Remove any nearby objects.

D
- Call 9-1-1 or the local emergency number.
- Follow basic precautions for preventing disease transmission.
- Care for life-threatening conditions.
- Monitor the airway, breathing, and circulation.
- Keep the victim comfortable.
- Do not give the victim anything to eat or drink.

- Wash the wound.
- Immobilize the injured area, keeping it lower than the heart, if possible.
- Care for life-threatening conditions.
- Monitor the airway, breathing, and circulation.
- Keep the victim comfortable.

Stings

Insect stings are painful. They can be fatal for some people who have severe allergic reactions. This allergic reaction may result in a breathing emergency. If someone is having a breathing emergency, call 9-1-1 or the local emergency number immediately.

To care for an insect sting—

- Follow basic precautions for preventing disease transmission.

- Examine the sting site to see if the stinger is in the skin (if there is one). If it is, scrape the stinger away from the skin with your fingernail or a plastic card, such as a credit card.
- Wash the wound.
- Apply a cold pack to the site.
- Care for life-threatening conditions.
- Monitor the airway, breathing, and circulation.
- Keep the victim comfortable.

Marine life

Many marine creatures, including some jellyfish, stingrays, some types of coral, and spiny urchins can sting people in the water. Your supervisor will tell you what kinds of marine life around your facility you should be concerned with.

If someone has been stung by marine life—

- Call 9-1-1 or the local emergency number if the victim was stung on the face or neck or is known to be allergic to marine life.
- Follow basic precautions for preventing disease transmission.
- Wash the wound.
- For a jellyfish sting—Soak the area with household vinegar, baking soda mixed in water, or rubbing alcohol as soon as possible.
- For a stingray sting—Immobilize the injured area and soak it in nonscalding water, as hot as the victim can stand, for 30 minutes.
- Care for life-threatening conditions.
- Monitor the airway, breathing, and circulation.
- Keep the victim comfortable.

Poisoning—Special Situations

Poisonous plants

Poison ivy, poison oak, and poison sumac are the most common poisonous plants (Fig. 7-4). Some people are allergic to these plants and have life-threatening reactions after contact, while others may not even get a rash.

- If someone has come in contact with a poisonous plant—
- Follow basic precautions to prevent disease transmission.
- Wash the area thoroughly with soap and water.
- If rash or wet blisters develop, advise the victim to see their doctor.
- If the condition spreads to large areas of the body or face, seek medical attention.

Inhaled poison

Poisonous fumes can come from a variety of sources. They may or may not have an odor. Common inhaled poisons include—

Fig. 7-4

- Carbon monoxide (car exhaust, fires, charcoal grills).
- Chlorine gas (highly toxic, requires training on how to recognize and deal with it).

If someone has inhaled poisonous fumes—

- Check to see if it is safe for you to help.
- Call 9-1-1 or the local emergency number.
- Follow basic precautions to prevent disease transmission.
- Move the victim to fresh air.
- Care for life-threatening conditions.
- Monitor the airway, breathing, and circulation.
- If conscious, keep the victim comfortable.

My Local Poison Control Number _____

Wounds

An injury to the body's soft tissue, such as the skin, fat, and muscles, is called a wound. Internal bleeding may occur when the soft tissue is damaged under the skin, as in a bruise. External bleeding occurs when there is a break in the skin's surface, such as a cut.

Burns are a kind of soft tissue injury. A burn occurs when intense heat, certain chemicals, electricity, or radiation contacts the skin or other body tissues.

Caring for Internal Bleeding

Most internal wounds do not require special medical care. However, if a person complains of severe pain or cannot move a body part without pain or if you think a great force caused the injury, call 9-1-1 or the local emergency number immediately. While waiting for EMS personnel to arrive—

- Follow basic precautions for preventing disease transmission.
- Care for any life-threatening conditions first.
- Monitor the airway, breathing, and circulation.
- Watch for changes in consciousness.
- Keep the victim comfortable and reassure the victim.
- Keep the victim from getting chilled or overheated.
- Care for any other problems that develop, such as vomiting.

If the wound is not serious—

1. Follow basic precautions for preventing disease transmission.

2. Put direct pressure on the area to decrease bleeding under the skin.

3. Elevate the injured part to reduce swelling if you do not suspect a muscle, bone, or joint injury.

4. Put a cold pack on the area to help control both swelling and pain.

Caring for External Bleeding

To care for external bleeding, follow the general procedures for injury or sudden illness on land and—

- Follow basic precautions to prevent disease transmission.
- Cover the wound with a dressing, such as a sterile gauze pad.
- Put direct pressure firmly against the wound.
- Elevate the injured area above the heart only if you do not suspect a broken bone.
- Cover the dressing with a roller bandage and tie the knot directly over the wound.
- If the bleeding does not stop—
    - Apply more dressings and bandages on top of the first ones.
    - Use a pressure point to squeeze the artery.
    - Call, or have someone else call, 9-1-1 or the local emergency number.
- Care for shock.

Shock

Any serious injury or illness can cause the condition known as shock. Shock is a natural reaction by the body. It usually means the victim's condition is very serious. Signs and symptoms of shock include—

- Restlessness or irritability.
- Changes in consciousness.
- Pale or ashen, cool, moist skin.
- Rapid breathing.
- Rapid pulse.

Take steps to minimize the effects of shock:

- Make sure 9-1-1 or the local emergency number has been called.
- Monitor the victim's airway, breathing, and circulation (ABCs).
- Control any external bleeding.
- Keep the victim from getting chilled or overheated.
- Elevate the legs about 12 inches if a head, neck, or back injury or broken bones in the hips or legs are not suspected.
- Comfort and reassure the victim until EMS personnel arrive and take over.

Lifeguarding Tip: *DO NOT GIVE FOOD OR DRINK TO A VICTIM OF SHOCK.*

Care for Wounds—Special Situations

Many kinds of wounds can occur at aquatic facilities, such as severed body parts, embedded objects, or injuries to the mouth. In such situations, remain calm and follow the general procedures for injury or sudden illness on land and the following guidelines.

Lifeguarding Tip: *Always follow basic precautions to prevent disease transmission when providing care.*

Eye Injury

- Help the victim into a comfortable position.
- Do not try to remove any object from the eye.
- Place a sterile dressing around the object.
- Stabilize the object as best as you can.
- Apply a bandage around the object. Do not cover the uninjured eye. (Fig. 7-5).
- Never put direct pressure on the eyeball.

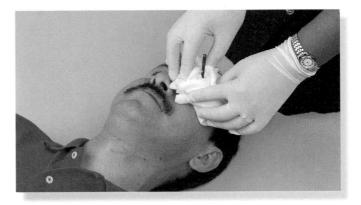

Fig. 7-5

Injuries to the Mouth and Teeth

- To control the bleeding inside the cheek, put folded dressings inside the mouth against the wound.
- To control bleeding on the outside of the cheek, use dressings to put pressure directly on the wound and bandage it so that it does not restrict breathing (Fig. 7-6).

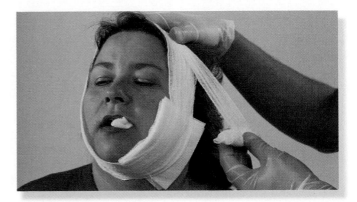

Fig. 7-6

- If a tooth is knocked out, put a sterile dressing in the space left by the tooth. Have the victim bite down on it gently to put pressure on the dressing. Preserve the tooth by placing it in a closed container of cool, fresh milk. If milk is not available, use water. Handle the tooth by the crown (chewing edge) and not the root. Do not clean the tooth. Advise the victim to get to a dentist with the tooth as soon as possible.

Injuries to the Abdomen

- Wounds through the abdomen can cause internal organs to push out.
- Carefully remove clothing from around the wound.
- Do not attempt to put the organs back into the abdomen.
- Cover the organs with a moist, sterile dressing and cover the dressing with plastic wrap.
- Place a folded towel or cloth over the dressing to keep the organs warm.
- Care for shock.

Nosebleed

- Have the victim lean forward and pinch the nostrils together until the bleeding stops.

Severed Body Parts

1. Control bleeding.
2. Wrap a severed body part(s) in sterile gauze (or clean material), put in a plastic bag, and put the bag on ice (Fig. 7-7).
3. Care for shock.
4. Be sure the body part is taken to the hospital with the victim immediately.

Fig. 7-7

Animal and Human Bites

An animal or human bite may be serious because of the wound and the risk of infection.

- Call 9-1-1 or the local emergency number if the wound bleeds severely or if you suspect the animal may have rabies.
- For severe bleeding - Control the bleeding first. Do not clean the wound; it will be properly cleaned at the hospital.

If the bleeding is minor—

- Wash the wound with soap and water.
- Control bleeding.
- Cover with a sterile bandage.

Emergency Childbirth

If a pregnant woman is about to give birth—

- Call 9-1-1 or the local emergency number.
- Important information to give to the dispatcher:
  - Her name, age, and expected due date
  - How long she has been having labor pains
  - If this is her first child
- Talk with the woman to help her remain calm.
- Place layers of newspaper covered with layers of linens, towels, or blankets under her.
- Control the scene so that the woman will have privacy.
- Position the woman on her back with her knees bent, feet flat, and legs spread apart.
- Remember, the woman delivers the baby, so be patient and let it happen naturally.
- The baby will be slippery; avoid dropping the baby.
- Wrap the baby in a clean, warm blanket or towel and place the baby next to the mother.

Lifeguarding Tips:

Do not let the woman get up or leave to find a bathroom (most women at this moment feel a desire to use the restroom).

Do not hold her knees together, this will not slow the birth process and may complicate the birth or harm the baby.

Do not place your fingers in the vagina for any reason.

Do not pull on the baby.

Scalp injuries

Scalp injuries often bleed heavily. Putting pressure on the area around the wound can control the bleeding.

- Apply pressure gently at first because there may be a skull fracture (Fig. 7-8). If you feel a depression, spongy areas, or bone fragments, do not put direct pressure on the wound.
- Call 9-1-1 or the local emergency number if you are unsure how serious a scalp injury is.

- For an open wound with no sign of a fracture, control the bleeding with several dressings secured with a bandage.

Embedded objects

An object that remains in an open wound is called an embedded object.

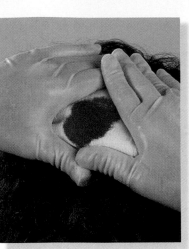

Fig. 7-8

- Call 9-1-1 or the local emergency number.
- Place several dressings around the object to keep it from moving.
- Bandage the dressings in place around the object (Fig. 7-9).
- Do not remove the object.

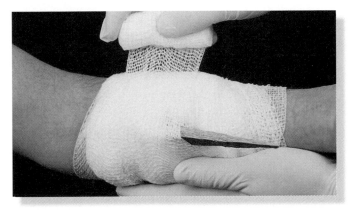

Fig. 7-9

Burns

There are four types of burns: heat, radiation, chemical, and electrical. How severe a burn is depends on—

- The temperature or strength of the heat or other source.
- The length of exposure to the burn source.
- The location of the burn.
- The area and size of the burn.
- The victim's age and general medical condition.

The following burns can lead to shock and need immediate medical attention:

- Burns that cause a victim to have difficulty breathing, or signs of burns around the mouth and nose

- Burns covering more than one body part or 10 percent of an adult's body surface
- Burns on the head, neck, hands, feet, or genitals
- Burns on a child or elderly person
- Burns on victims with a serious medical condition, such as diabetes
- Burns from chemicals, explosions, or electricity

Caring for Burns

Follow the general procedures for a land emergency to care for burns. If the scene is safe, check the victim for life-threatening conditions. Call 9-1-1 or the local emergency number if the condition is life threatening.

To care for burns—

- Follow basic precautions to prevent disease transmission.
- Cool the burned area with cool water.
- Cover the burned area with dry, sterile dressings. Loosely bandage the dressings in place.
- Take steps to minimize shock.

To care for electrical burns—

- Call 9-1-1 or the local emergency number.
- Check the scene for safety, and check for life-threatening injuries. If a power line is down, wait for the fire department or the power company to turn the power off.
- Follow basic precautions to prevent disease transmission.
- Do not cool the burn. (Because electrical burns usually involve nerve damage, the victim may not feel pain and cooling the burn achieves little.)
- Cover the burn with a dry, sterile dressing.
- Take steps to minimize shock.

To care for chemical burns—

- Follow basic precautions to prevent disease transmission.
- Call 9-1-1 or the local emergency number.
- Flush the affected area continuously with large amounts of water. Brush off dry chemicals with a gloved hand, being careful not to get the chemical on you or to brush it into the victim's eyes.
- Keep flushing the area until EMS personnel arrive.
- If a chemical gets into the eyes, flush the eyes with cool, clean running water until EMS personnel arrive. Always flush the affected eye from the nose outward and downward to prevent washing the chemical into the other eye.

Injuries to Muscles, Bones, and Joints

Injuries to muscles, bones, and joints can happen from accidents, such as falls. There are four types of muscle, bone, and joint injuries: fractures, dislocations, sprains, and strains. It is difficult to know whether a muscle, bone, or joint injury is a fracture, dislocation, sprain, or strain. You do not need to know the type of injury because the care you give is the same.

BURN ACTIVITY

Directions: Write down what you would do in the following situations.

- Scenario 1

The Facts: A co-worker drops a bottle that contains a chemical agent. The bottle hits the edge of the counter and breaks. The chemical agent splashes on the skin of her bare arm. The chemical agent is burning her skin. What do you do?

_____

_____

_____

- Scenario 2

The Facts: Today your facility is having an end-of-the-season party and barbecue. While a co-worker is putting lighter fluid on the charcoal, someone throws a match into the barbecue pit. The person with the lighter fluid screams as his hand and arm catches fire. You put out the fire by using a towel. His arm has deep burns with blisters. What do you do?

_____

_____

_____

- Scenario 3

The Facts: At your facility, an electrician puts his hand on a live fuse box and gets an electric shock. He is thrown back several feet and has a severe charred burn on his hand. He is lying on the ground and is unconscious. What would you do?

_____

_____

_____

Caring for Muscle, Bone, and Joint Injuries

When caring for muscle, bone, and joint injuries, use the general procedures for a land emergency and—

- Follow basic precautions to prevent disease transmission.
- Call 9-1-1 or the local emergency number if the victim cannot move or use the injured area.
- Support the injured area above and below the site of the injury.
- Check for feeling, warmth, and color below the injured area.
- Immobilize and secure the injured area if the victim must be moved and it does not cause further pain or injury.
- Recheck for feeling, warmth, and color below the injured area.

Immobilizing Muscle, Bone, and Joint injuries

Immobilizing a muscle, bone, or joint injury helps keep the injured body part from moving. This may also help reduce any pain.

When immobilizing an injured body part:

- Immobilize the injured body part in the position you find it or in the position in which the victim is holding it.
- Immobilize the injured area and the bones and joints above and below the injury site.

Following are ways to immobilize common muscle, bone, and joint injuries:

Arm Injuries

- To make a sling, place a triangular bandage under the injured arm and over the uninjured shoulder to form a sling.
- Leave the arm in the position you find it or in the position in which the victim is holding it.
- Tie the ends of the sling at the side of the neck. Place gauze pads under the knots to make it more comfortable for the victim.
- Secure the arm to the chest with a folded triangular bandage.

Leg injury

- Immobilize an injured leg by binding it to the uninjured leg.

Foot injuries

- Immobilize the ankle and foot using a soft splint, such as a pillow or rolled blanket. Do not remove the victim's shoes.

Rib/Breastbone Injury

- Place a pillow or folded towel between the victim's injured ribs and arm.
- Bind the arm to the body to help support the injured area.

Hand and Finger Injuries

- Put a bulky dressing on the area. For injuries to a finger, tape the injured finger to the finger next to it.

Caring for Open Fractures

An open fracture occurs when a broken bone tears through the skin and surrounding soft tissue. To care for a victim with an open fracture—

- Place sterile dressings around the open fracture as you would for an embedded object.
- Bandage the dressings in place around the fracture.
- Do not move the exposed bone and limb; this may cause the victim great pain and may worsen the injury.

Injuries to the Head, Neck, or Back

If you suspect that a victim has a head, neck, or back injury, tell him or her not to nod or shake his or her head but to say yes or no. The goal is to minimize movement. To care for injuries to the head, neck, or back—

- Follow basic precautions to prevent disease transmission.
- Minimize movement of the victim's head, neck, and back by putting your hands on both sides of the victim's head. Maintain an open airway. Have the victim remain in the position that you found him or her until EMS personnel arrives and take over.
- Monitor the airway, breathing, and circulation.

Lifeguarding Tip: *An important part of a lifeguard's job is to recognize and care for head, neck, or back injuries. If you encounter a patron who is standing with a suspected head, neck, or back injury, do not have the person sit or lie down. Immobilize the victim's head by applying in-line stabilization where you find him or her. If the victim complains of dizziness or begins to lose consciousness, slowly lower the victim to the ground, while maintaining in-line stabilization. Ask other lifeguards for help. For additional information on head, neck, or back injuries, see Chapter 8.*

Heat- and Cold-Related Emergencies

Exposure to extreme heat or cold can make a person ill. A person can develop a heat- or cold-related illness even when temperatures are not extreme. Whether such emergencies occur also depends on the person's physical activity, the wind, humidity, general working or living conditions, and age and state of health.

Once the signs and symptoms of a heat- or cold-related illness appear, the victim's condition can quickly get worse and even lead to death. The chart below lists the signs and symptoms and care to give victims of heat- and cold-related emergencies.

Heat-Related Emergencies

Signals	Care
Heat Cramps - Painful muscle spasms, usually in the legs and abdomen	- Have the victim move to a cool place. - Give cool water to drink. - Have the victim lightly stretch the muscle and gently massage the area.
Heat Exhaustion - Cool, moist, pale, flushed, or ashen skin - Headache, nausea, dizziness - Weakness, exhaustion	- Move the victim to a cooler environment. - Loosen or remove clothing. - Fan the victim. - Get the victim into circulating air while cooling the victim's body with water using a cloth or sponge. - If the victim is conscious, give small amounts of cool water to drink. - If the victim's condition does not improve or if you suspect heat stroke, call 9-1-1 or the local emergency number.
Heat Stroke - A life-threatening condition - A change in the level of consciousness - High body temperature - Red, hot skin that can be either dry or moist - Rapid or weak pulse - Rapid or shallow breathing	- Call 9-1-1 or the local emergency number. - Give the same care as for heat exhaustion until help arrives.

Cold-Related Emergencies	
Signals	**Care**
Hypothermia ■ Shivering ■ Slow, irregular pulse ■ Numbness ■ Glassy stare ■ Apathy or unclear thinking ■ Loss of muscle control, no shivering, loss of consciousness (in late stage of hypothermia)	■ Gently move the victim to a warm place. ■ Monitor the victim's airway, breathing, and circulation and care for shock. ■ Remove wet clothing and cover the victim with blankets and plastic sheeting to hold in the victim's body heat. ■ Warm the victim slowly and handle the victim carefully.
Frostbite ■ Loss of feeling and sensation in the extremity ■ Discolored, waxy skin appearance ■ Severe frostbite may include blisters and blue skin	■ Remove wet clothing and jewelry from the affected area. ■ Soak the frostbitten area in warm (not hot) water. ■ Cover with dry, sterile dressings—do not rub the area. ■ Monitor the victim's airway, breathing, and circulation and care for shock. ■ Do not rewarm a frostbitten part if there is a danger of it refreezing.

Putting it All Together

You may see a variety of injuries and illnesses in an aquatic environment. People can be injured and become ill in many ways, and part of your job is to give effective care to them. Follow general procedures for injury or sudden illness on land until EMS personnel arrive and take over. Remember that you have a duty to respond, and your role is important for the safety and well-being of patrons at your facility.

PUTTING IT ALL TOGETHER ACTIVITY

Directions: Read the following scenario and answer the following question using the FIND model.

The Facts: A young boy runs into the men's locker room. As he enters, he runs into another boy. The impact throws each child backwards. One child is lying flat on his back and appears to be unconscious. The other is crying and screaming that his arm hurts. How would you handle this situation using the FIND model?

Figure out the problem and write it below.

Identify possible solutions for the problem and write them below.

1.

2.

3.

Name pros and cons for each possible solution and write them below.

Pros:

Cons:

Pros:

Cons:

Pros:

Cons:

Decide which solution is best and write it below.

in review...

Circle the letter of the correct answer or answers.

1. **Signs and symptoms of sudden illness can include—**
   a. Changes in skin color.
   b. Slurred speech.
   c. Dizziness.
   d. Nausea or vomiting.

2. **Use a pressure point to control bleeding—**
   a. Immediately.
   b. By placing a sterile dressing over the wound.
   c. Before elevating the wound above the heart.
   d. By squeezing the artery against the bone beneath it.

3. **When caring for a shock victim, you should not—**
   a. Have the victim lie down.
   b. Elevate the victim's legs.
   c. Cover the victim to prevent chilling.
   d. Give the victim anything to eat or drink.

4. **Once you have wrapped a severed body part and placed it in a plastic bag, you should—**
   a. Keep it warm by holding it next to your skin.
   b. Keep it cool by placing the bag on ice.
   c. Put the bag in the freezer.
   d. Put ice in the bag.

5. **Cool burned areas immediately with—**
   a. Cool water.
   b. Ice water.
   c. Pain relief spray.
   d. Burn ointment.

6. **With heat-related illnesses, call EMS personnel immediately if the victim—**
   a. Has cool, moist, pale, or red skin.
   b. Refuses water.
   c. Vomits.
   d. Undergoes a change in the level of consciousness.

7. **Signs of hypothermia include—**
   a. Numbness.
   b. Glassy stare.
   c. Nausea.
   d. Increased heart rate.

Circle True or False.

8. **After you have splinted an injured body part, the victim can be left alone until EMS personnel arrive.**

   True   False

9. **If you suspect someone is having a diabetic emergency, under no circumstances allow that person to have sugar.**

   True   False

10. **When caring for frostbite, warm the area as quickly as possible by rubbing it.**

    True   False

11. **If a person has been poisoned, general care includes making the victim vomit.**

    True   False

12. **If a victim is suffering from hypothermia, you should not warm the body too quickly.**

    True   False

13. **Put the following basic care steps for burns in correct sequence (number 1-3):**
    ___ Minimize shock.
    ___ Cover the burned area.
    ___ Cool the burned area (unless caused by electricity).

14. **Rate the following from least severe (1) to most severe (3).**
    ___ Heat exhaustion.
    ___ Heat stroke.
    ___ Heat cramps.

controlling bleeding

Remember: Always follow basic precautions to prevent disease transmission.

1. Survey the scene and then check the victim.

   - Identify yourself and ask the victim if you may help.
   - Take basic precautions to prevent disease transmission.

Remember: Be sure to get permission before caring for a conscious child. Tell the child's parent or guardian your level of training and the care you are going to provide

2. Cover the wound with a dressing.

   - Press firmly against the wound (direct pressure).

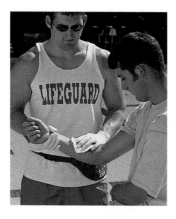

3. Elevate the injured area—

   - Above the level of the heart.
   - Only when you suspect that a bone is not broken.

4. Cover the dressing with a roller bandage.

   - Tie the knot directly over the wound.

5. If bleeding does not stop—

   - Apply more dressings and bandages on top of the first ones.
   - Use a pressure point to squeeze the artery against the bone.

   - Call, or have someone else call, 9-1-1 or the local emergency number.
   - Care for shock.

applying a sling and binder

Remember: Always follow basic precautions to prevent disease transmission.

1. Survey the scene and then check the victim.

   ■ Identify yourself and ask the victim if you may help.

   ■ Take basic precautions to prevent disease transmission.

   Remember: Be sure to get permission before caring for a conscious child. Tell the child's parent or guardian your level of training and the care you are going to provide.

2. If the victim is unable to move or use an injured arm—Call, or have someone else call, 9-1-1 or the local emergency number.

   NOTE: Splint a victim only if the victim must be moved and it does not cause further pain or injury.

3. Position of injured arm.

   ■ Leave the arm in the position you find it or in the position in which the victim is holding it.

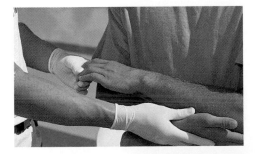

4. Check for feeling, warmth, and color below the injured area.

5. Place the sling.

   ■ Place a triangular bandage under the injured arm and over the uninjured shoulder to form a sling.

   ■ Leave the arm in the position you find it.

6. Tie ends of sling at side of neck.

Lifeguarding Tip: Place pads of gauze under the knots to make it more comfortable for the victim.

7. Secure injured area.

   ■ Secure the arm to the chest with a folded triangular bandage.

8. Recheck for feeling, warmth, and color below the injured area.

head, neck, and back injuries on land

Remember: Always take basic precautions to prevent disease transmission.

1. Survey the scene and then check the victim.

   - Identify yourself and ask the victim if you may help.
   - Take basic precautions to prevent disease transmission.

   Remember: Be sure to get permission before caring for a conscious child. Tell the child's parent or guardian your level of training and the care you are going to provide.

2. If you think the victim has a head, neck, or back injury—
   Call, or have someone else call, 9-1-1 or the local emergency number.

3. Minimize movement of the head, neck, and back.

   - Place your hands on both sides of the victim's head and support the victim's head as you find it.

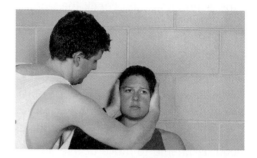

Lifeguarding Tip: If the head is sharply turned to one side, do not try to align it. Support the head as you find it.

4. Monitor the airway, breathing, and circulation.

caring

for head, neck, and back injuries in the water

You are on the lifeguard stand when you see a man dive into the shallow end of the pool. He seems to be struggling and cannot lift his head out of the water. He is facedown, just below the surface, in about 4 feet of water. Do you recognize this as a possible head, neck, or back injury? Would you be ready to give the right care? Every year, there are 10,000 spinal cord injuries in the U.S. About 7 percent of these injuries occur during sports and recreation, some from diving into shallow water.[1] This chapter describes how to prevent, recognize, and care for possible head, neck, or back injuries.

Preventing Head, Neck, and Back Injuries in Water

Head, neck, and back injuries rarely happen during supervised diving into deep water. Most injuries happen during unsupervised activity. In pools, head, neck, or back injuries most often happen—

- At the shallow end, in a corner, or where the bottom slopes from shallow to deep water.
- During the patron's first visit to the facility.
- When someone strikes a floating object, like an inner tube, while diving.

[1] The Spinal Cord Injury Information Network, June 2000

At lakes, rivers, or oceans, head, neck, and back injuries usually occur—

- Where depths change with the tide or current.
- When someone plunges headfirst into shallow water or a breaking wave and his or her head hits the bottom.
- While body surfing, bodyboarding, or surfing.
- From collisions with underwater hazards, such as a rock, tree stump, or sandbar.

Many people die each year from head, neck, or back injuries and many more are permanently disabled. The following guidelines will help prevent head, neck, and back injuries:

- Check the water depth before diving (minimum of 9 feet deep).
- Enter the water feet first.
- Never dive into an above-ground pool.
- Only trained swimmers should use starting blocks under a coach's supervision.
- Place starting blocks above deep water (at least 9 feet deep).
- Never use alcohol or other drugs and dive.
- Never dive into water where you cannot see the bottom.
- Do not run into shallow water and dive headfirst.

When bodysurfing, bodyboarding, or surfing, always keep your arms in front of you to protect your head, neck, and back when going underwater.

Causes of Head, Neck, and Back Injuries

Always think that a head, neck, or back injury might have happened in the following situations:

- Any headfirst entry into shallow water
- A fall onto land from a height greater than the victim's height
- An injury involving a diving board or water slide
- A person entering water from a height, such as a bank, cliff, or tower

Signs and symptoms of possible head, neck, or back injury include—

- Head, neck or back pain, loss of balance, or difficulty breathing.
- Loss of body movement below the injury site.
- Tingling or loss of sensation in the arms, legs, hands, or feet.
- Bumps, bruises, or depressions on the head, neck, or back.
- Altered consciousness, seizures, or fluid or blood in the ears.
- Complete or partial inability to move the arms and legs.

Victims with a head, neck, or back injury may behave in different ways:

- The victim briefly swims or struggles at the surface before submerging.
- The victim hangs onto the side of the pool and then walks out of the water holding his or her neck or head.
- The victim cannot exhale forcefully enough to clear water from the airway, even when conscious.

Caring for Head, Neck, and Back Injuries

If you recognize that a victim has the signs and symptoms of a possible head, neck, or back injury—

- Stabilize and immobilize the area.
- Keep the victim as still as possible until EMS personnel arrive.
- Always give care as if the spine is injured, even if you are not sure.

The care you give a victim with a head, neck, or back injury in the water depends on—

- The victim's condition, including whether he or she is breathing and shows signs of circulation.
- The location of the victim (shallow or deep water, at the surface of the water, underwater, or not in the water).
- The availability of help, such as other lifeguards, bystanders, fire fighters, police, or EMS personnel.
- Your facility's specific procedures.
- The air and water temperature.

Rescue Guidelines for Head, Neck, or Back Injuries

If you suspect a head, neck, or back injury, activate the EAP and follow these general rescue procedures:

1. **Survey the scene and safely enter the water.** Choose the best type of entry based on the following factors:

- Water depth
- Your height above the water
- Location of the victim
- Facility design

Lifeguarding Tip: If the victim is near the side of the pool wall, do not perform a compact jump or stride jump. Instead, simply ease into the water. Sit on the pool deck (facing the water) and gently slide into the water.

2. **Determine the victim's condition.** Determine if the victim is at the surface or submerged.

3. **Perform an appropriate rescue.** Swim to the victim to make contact and use an in-line stabilization technique to minimize movement of the victim's head, neck, and back. Use an appropriate in-line stabilization technique based on the victim's location and whether the victim is face-up or face-down.

4. **Move the victim to safety.** Once you have stabilized the victim, move the victim to shallow water, if possible.

5. **Remove the victim from the water.** Immobilize the victim on a backboard and remove the victim from the water.

Lifeguarding Tip: Check for consciousness and breathing. If the victim is not breathing or shows no signs of circulation, immediately remove the victim from the water using a backboard.

6. **Provide emergency care as needed.** Once the victim is out of the water—

- Use basic precautions to prevent disease transmission. Use disposable gloves and breathing devices.

- Give rescue breathing, first aid, or CPR, if needed.

- Monitor the airway, breathing, and circulation.

- Minimize shock by keeping the victim from getting chilled or overheated.

- Administer oxygen or use an automated external defibrillator (AED) if needed and if you are trained to do so.

Fig. 8-1A

In-line stabilization techniques

Two different techniques are used in the water to minimize movement of the victim's head and neck: the head splint and the head and chin support. Both can be used in shallow or deep water and with face-up or face-down victims at or near the surface.

Head splint

The head splint is used for a face-down or face-up victim, at or near the surface, in shallow or deep water. In deep water, use the rescue tube to help keep you and the victim afloat.

To perform the head splint technique on a face-down victim in shallow or deep water at or near the surface—

1. Approach the victim from the side.

2. Grasp the victim's arms midway between the shoulder and elbow. Grasp the victim's right arm with your right hand and the victim's left arm with your left hand. Gently move the victim's arms up alongside the head.

Fig. 8-1B

3. Squeeze the victim's arms against his or her head to help hold the head in line with the body (Fig. 8-1A).

4. Glide the victim slowly forward. If you are in shallow water, lower yourself to shoulder depth before you begin gliding the victim forward. Continue moving slowly and turn the victim toward you until he or she is face-up. Do this by pushing the victim's arm that is closer to you under the water while pulling the victim's other arm across the surface toward you (Fig. 8-1B).

5. Position the victim's head close to the crook of your arm, with the head in line with the body (Fig. 8-1C).

6. Hold the victim in this position until help arrives.

To perform the head splint technique on a face-up victim in shallow or deep water at or near the surface—

Fig. 8-1C

1. Approach the victim's head from behind, or stand behind the victim's head. In shallow water, lower your body so that the water level is at your neck.

2. Grasp the victim's arms midway between the shoulder and elbow with your thumbs to the inside of each of the victim's arms (Fig. 8-2 A-B). Grasp the victim's right arm with your right hand and the victim's left arm with your left hand. Gently move the victim's arms up alongside the head and reposition yourself to the victim's side as you trap the victim's head with his or her arms.

3. Slowly and carefully squeeze the victim's arms against his or her head to help hold the head in line with the body (Fig. 8-2 C-D). Do not move the victim any more than you have to.

4. Position the victim's head close to the crook of your arm, with the head in line with the body (Fig. 8-2 E-F).

5. Hold the victim in this position until help arrives.

Fig. 8-2A

Fig. 8-2B

Fig. 8-2C

Fig. 8-2D

Fig. 8-2E

Fig. 8-2F

Head and chin support

The head and chin support is used for face-down or face-up victims, at or near the surface, in shallow water at least 3 feet deep or in deep water. The head and chin support is also used to rescue submerged victims in deep water. In deep water, use the rescue tube for support only after you have safely stabilized and positioned the victim face-up (Fig. 8-3). The head and chin support technique is not used in all situations:

- Do not use the head and chin support for a face-down victim in water less than 3 feet deep. This technique requires you to submerge and roll under the victim while maintaining in-line stabilization. It is difficult to do this in water less than 3 feet deep without risking injury to you or the victim.

- Do not use the rescue tube for support when performing the head and chin support on a face-down victim in deep water. This impedes your ability to turn the victim over.

To perform the head and chin support for a face-up or face-down victim in shallow water at or near the surface—

1. Approach the victim from the side.

2. With your body at about shoulder depth in the water, place one forearm along the length of the victim's breastbone and the other forearm along the victim's spine.

3. Use your hands to gently hold the victim's head and neck in line with the body. Place one hand on the victim's lower jaw and the other hand on the back of the lower head (Fig. 8-4 A-B). Be careful not to touch the back of the neck.

4. Squeeze your forearms together, clamping the victim's chest and back. Continue to support the victim's head and neck.

   - If the victim is face-down, you must turn him or her face-up. Using the head and chin support to stabilize the spine, slowly move the victim forward to help lift the victim's legs. Turn the victim toward you as you submerge (Fig. 8-4C).

Fig. 8-3

Fig. 8-4A

Fig. 8-4B

Fig. 8-4C

Fig. 8-4D

Fig. 8-4E

- Roll under the victim while turning the victim over (Fig. 8-4D). Avoid twisting the victim's body. The victim is face-up when you surface on the other side (Fig. 8-4E).

5. Hold the victim face up in the water until help arrives.

Submerged Victims

You can also use the head and chin support for a submerged victim found face-up, face-down, or on one side. Follow the general steps for the head and chin support while you bring the victim to the surface at an angle:

- Turn the victim face-up, if needed, as you move to the surface (Fig. 8-5A).

Fig. 8-5A

Fig. 8-5B

- After you use the head and chin support, turn the victim faceup, and stabilize the victim at the surface (Fig. 8-5B). Another lifeguard places the rescue tube under your armpits to help keep the victim and you afloat.

Using the Backboard

At least two lifeguards are needed to immobilize a victim on a backboard, but additional lifeguards or bystanders should also help if available. Backboards come in different shapes and sizes. They vary in materials, the number and size of handholds, and their buoyancy (Fig. 8-6). Be familiar with the equipment at your facility. Practice backboarding techniques regularly during in-service training to keep up your skills.

After stabilizing the victim's head and neck with either the head splint or the head and chin support, immobilize the victim on a backboard. Follow these steps to immobilize a victim in shallow water:

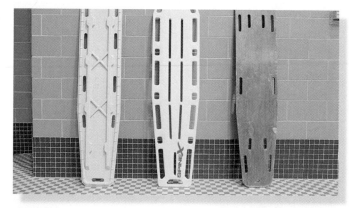

Fig. 8-6

1. The FIRST lifeguard brings the victim to the side of the pool using the head and chin support or head splint. The SECOND lifeguard enters the water, submerges the backboard, and positions it under the victim so that it extends slightly beyond the victim's head (Fig. 8-7 A-B).

2. While the SECOND lifeguard raises the backboard into place, the FIRST lifeguard carefully removes his or her arm from beneath the victim.

Head Splint Technique	Head and Chin Support
■ The FIRST lifeguard moves the arm that is under the victim toward the top of the victim's head and continues to apply pressure on both arms, while the SECOND lifeguard uses the head and chin support to stabilize the victim (one hand and arm on the chin and chest, the other hand and arm under the backboard) (Fig.8-8). ■ Once the backboard is in place, the FIRST lifeguard lowers the victim's arms, moves to the victim's head, submerges to shoulder depth, and supports the backboard against his or her chest and shoulders while squeezing the sides of the backboard with his or her forearms. The FIRST lifeguard then stabilizes the victim's head by placing his or her hands along each side of the victim's head (see Fig. 8-9B).	■ The FIRST lifeguard keeps the hand on the chin and arm on the chest and places the other hand and arm under the backboard (Fig. 8-9A). ■ Once the backboard is in place, the SECOND lifeguard moves to the victim's head, submerges to shoulder depth, supports the backboard against his or her chest and shoulders, and squeezes the sides of the backboard with his or her forearms. The SECOND lifeguard then stabilizes the victim's head by placing his or her hands along each side of the victim's head (Fig. 8-9B).

Fig. 8-7A

Fig. 8-7B

Fig. 8-8

Fig. 8-9A

Fig. 8-9B

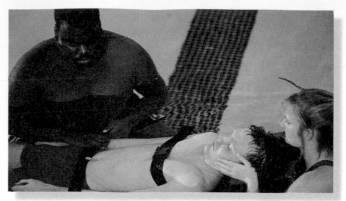

Fig. 8-10B

Lifeguarding Tip: Use rescue tubes under the foot and head of the backboard for flotation if needed.

3. The lifeguard who is not positioned at the victim's head secures the victim on the backboard. The lifeguard places straps at least across the victim's chest, hips, and thighs. Secure the straps in the following order:

    a. Strap across the chest and under the victim's armpits. This helps prevent the victim from sliding on the backboard during the removal (Fig. 8-10A).

    b. Strap across the hips with the victim's arms and hands secured (Fig. 8-10B).

    c. Strap across the thighs (Fig. 8-10C).

    d. Recheck straps to be sure that they are secure.

4. After all the straps have been checked and properly secured, the lifeguard immobilizes the victim's head to the board, using a head immobilizer and a strap across the victim's forehead (Fig. 8-11).

Lifeguarding Tip: Different methods can be used to secure a victim to a backboard. Always be sure that you safely immobilize the victim's spine. Whatever method you use, secure the victim's body to the backboard before using the head immobilizer. Follow the manufacturers' directions.

Fig. 8-10C

Fig. 8-11

Removal from the Water

Once the victim is secured on the backboard, remove him or her from the water:

1. Position the backboard with the head end by the side of the pool and the foot end straight out into the pool. Use one or two rescue tubes if needed to support the foot end of the board.

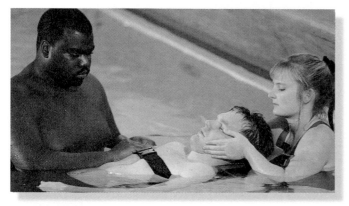

Fig. 8-10A

2. With one lifeguard at each side, lift the head of the backboard slightly and place it on the edge of the gutter, if possible (Fig. 8-12A).

3. One lifeguard gets out of the pool and grasps the head of the backboard. The other lifeguard helps lift the head end of the board onto the deck and then moves to the foot end of the backboard (Fig. 8-12B).

4. As the lifeguard on deck stands and steps backward pulling the backboard, the lifeguard at the foot end pushes on the backboard. Use proper lifting techniques to prevent injury:

- Keep your back straight.
- Bend at the knees.
- Move in a controlled way without jerking or tugging (Fig. 8-12C).

5. Together both lifeguards slide the backboard up over the edge of the deck out of and away from the water.

Anyone else helping stays in the water at the sides of the backboard and helps guide the backboard and victim onto the deck (Fig. 8-12D).

Life-threatening conditions

If you find that the injured victim is not breathing or shows no signs of circulation, immediately remove the victim from the water.

- Maintain in-line stabilization.
- Place the backboard under the victim.
- Remove the victim from the water using the two-person removal (see Chapter 5). Make every effort to minimize movement of the victim's head and neck.
- Do not waste time strapping the victim to the board because this would delay urgently needed care.

Once the victim is safely removed from the water—

- Use basic precautions to prevent disease transmission.Use disposable gloves and breathing barriers.
- Do a primary survey (airway, breathing, and circulation). Use the two-handed jaw-thrust technique to open the airway to minimize movement of the head, neck, and back.
- Give rescue breathing, first aid, or CPR if needed.
- Minimize shock by keeping the victim from getting chilled or overheated.
- Administer oxygen or use an AED (if needed and if you are trained to do so).

Fig. 8-12A

Fig. 8-12B

Fig. 8-12C

Fig. 8-12D

Caring for Head, Neck, or Back Injuries in Deep Water

Fortunately, head, neck, or back injuries rarely occur in deep water. If one does occur, you can often move the victim to shallow water. You may have to remove a lane line or safety line to reach shallow water. If you cannot move the victim to shallow water, such as in a separate diving well, use the rescue tube to help support you and the victim until help arrives. Additional lifeguards bringing the backboard can help support the victim. Use a platform attached to the deck, more rescue tubes, or personal flotation devices to give support.

To stabilize the victim's spine and secure the victim on the backboard in deep water, slightly modify the procedures used in shallow water:

1. To immobilize the victim on a backboard, the FIRST lifeguard moves the victim to the side of the pool, if possible toward the corner of the pool. The SECOND lifeguard places the backboard under the victim while the FIRST lifeguard keeps the victim's head in line with the head splint or the head and chin support for a face-up or submerged victim.

2. The lifeguard who is not positioned at the victim's head secures the victim on the backboard (Fig. 8-15). The lifeguard places straps at least across the victim's chest, hips, and thighs. After all the straps have been checked and properly secured, the lifeguard immobilizes the victim's head to the board, using a head immobilizer and a strap across the victim's forehead.

Head Splint Technique	**Head and Chin Support** **(Face-up or Submerged Victim)**
■ If the victim is at or near the surface, the FIRST lifeguard supports the victim's head and neck using the head splint technique (Fig. 8-13). ■ The FIRST lifeguard moves the arm that is under the victim toward the top of the victim's head and continues to apply pressure on both arms, while the SECOND lifeguard uses the head and chin support to stabilize the victim (one hand and arm on the chin and chest, the other hand and arm under the backboard). ■ Once the backboard is in place the FIRST lifeguard lowers the victim's arms, moves to the victim's head, and rests the backboard on the rescue tube while squeezing the sides of the backboard with his or her forearms. The FIRST lifeguard then stabilizes the victim's head by placing his or her hands along each side of the victim's head.	■ If the victim is submerged, the FIRST lifeguard leaves the rescue tube on the surface and do a feet-first surface dive to the victim. He or she brings the victim to the surface using the head and chin support (Fig 8-14A). The SECOND lifeguard retrieves the FIRST lifeguard's rescue tube and inserts it under the FIRST lifeguard's armpits (Fig. 8-14B). ■ The SECOND lifeguard retrieves the backboard and submerges it under the victim (Fig. 8-14C). ■ The FIRST lifeguard keeps the hand on the chin and arm on the chest and places the other hand and arm under the backboard. ■ Once the backboard is in place, the SECOND lifeguard moves to the victim's head, rests the backboard on the rescue tube, and squeezes the sides of the backboard with his or her forearms. The SECOND lifeguard then stabilizes the victim's head by placing his or her hands along each side of the victim's head (Fig. 8-14D).

Fig. 8-13

Fig. 8-14A

Fig. 8-14B

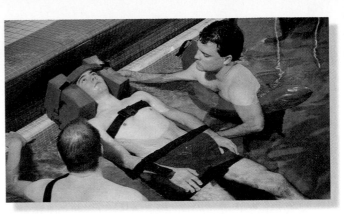

Fig. 8-15

Fig. 8-14C

Fig. 8-16

Caring for Head, Neck, or Back Injury in Extremely Shallow Water

Today many facilities have extremely shallow water areas such as zero-depth pools, wave pools, spray pools, and waterfront facilities. Caring for a victim of a head, neck, or back injury who is facedown in extremely shallow water (less than 2 feet) takes practice. Care is described in Chapters 9 or 10.

Putting it All Together

Lifeguards need to recognize and be able to care for victims with head, neck, or back injuries. To decide whether an injury could be serious, consider both its cause and the signs and symptoms. If you suspect a victim in the water has a head, neck, or back injury, make sure someone calls EMS immediately. Minimize movement by using in-line stabilization. Secure the victim to a backboard to immobilize the head and spine. Remove a victim from the water using proper lifting techniques to avoid injuring yourself. When the victim is out of the water, give care as needed until EMS personnel arrive.

Fig. 8-14D

3. Using proper lifting techniques, both lifeguards work together to remove the victim from the water (Fig. 8-16).

Lifeguarding Tip: Use rescue tubes in deep water for additional flotation for the backboard and rescuers.

in review...

Circle the letter of the best answer or answers.

1. In a pool, a head, neck, or back injury is most likely to occur—
   a. In the deep end.
   b. At the shallow end.
   c. Where the bottom slopes from shallow to deep water.
   d. When an individual strikes a floating object, such as an inner tube, while diving.

2. At a waterfront, a head, neck, or back injury is most likely to occur—
   a. When a swimmer runs into the water and plunges headfirst into breaking waves.
   b. When a swimmer collides with an underwater hazard, such as a sandbar.
   c. In an area where the water level almost never varies.
   d. When a swimmer plunges headfirst into shallow water.

3. Which of the following situations indicate a possible head, neck, or back injury?
   a. An injury resulting from diving off a diving board
   b. A headfirst entry into shallow water
   c. A fall from a height greater than the victim's height
   d. A sudden cramp in deep water
   e. An injury after entering the water from a cliff

4. Which of the following signs and symptoms indicate a possible head, neck, or back injury?
   a. Neck or back pain
   b. Loss of body movement
   c. Difficulty breathing
   d. Loss of balance
   e. Fluid or blood in the ears

5. A swimmer is injured while body surfing and complains of tingling and loss of sensation in both legs. You should—
   a. Massage the area vigorously.
   b. Keep the victim as still as possible until more advanced help arrives.
   c. Begin rescue breathing.
   d. Have the victim try to walk out of the water.

6. The _____ is used only for a victim found face-down at or near the surface of deep water.
   a. Head splint technique.
   b. Head and chin support.

Circle True or False

7. For a head, neck, or back injury in deep water, do not waste time trying to stabilize the head and neck until you have the victim on shore.

   True   False

8. Several lifeguards are more effective for immobilizing and removing a victim from deep water.

   True   False

chapter 9

waterfront
lifeguarding

Waterfronts are open-water areas, such as lakes, rivers, ponds, and oceans (Fig. 9-1). This chapter covers nonsurf open-water areas, such as at national and state parks, summer camps, and campgrounds. This chapter does not discuss lifeguarding at surf environments where strong waves or strong currents are present. Surf lifeguarding requires other specialized skills.

Much of the information and skills you have learned in previous chapters also apply directly to waterfront settings. The importance of professionalism, teamwork, public relations, and many rescue skills is unchanged. If it has been a while since you read Chapters 1 through 8, you may want to review that material before reading this chapter.

Every waterfront is unique. They vary in water quality, clarity, currents, and beach conditions. Lifeguards learn the unique aspects of their facility through orientation and in-service training. Fully understanding conditions at your facility helps you prevent injuries.

Injury Prevention

Injury prevention strategies at waterfronts are similar to those used at pools. But lifeguards adjust patron and facility surveillance techniques for the particular waterfront.

Rules and regulations

At waterfronts, as at pools, rules and regulations are important for everyone's safety. In your orientation and

Fig. 9-1

in-service training, you will learn the facility's rules and regulations. Rules posted at waterfronts should include—

- Swim only when a lifeguard is on duty.
- Obey lifeguard instructions at all times.
- Swim only in designated areas.
- No running, pushing, or horseplay.
- No playing or swimming under piers, rafts, platforms, or play structures.
- No boats, sailboards, surfboards, or personal water craft in swimming areas.
- Dive only in designated areas.
- No running or diving head-first into shallow water.
- No glass containers in the beach area.
- No alcohol or other drug use.
- No fishing near swimming areas.
- Stay off lifeguard stands.

Always remember to enforce rules fairly and in a positive manner. Be able to explain reasons for the rules. If you do not know the reason for a rule, ask your supervisor.

Facility Surveillance

You must know the potential hazards at a waterfront, such as—

- Underwater obstructions.
- Poor water quality or clarity.
- Currents.
- Changing weather conditions.
- Plants and animals in the water.

Be particularly aware of dangerous conditions that may change with the wind, tides, and weather. On some days, the water may be totally calm and flat. Other days, there may be large waves. Adjust your surveillance techniques to make sure you can see everyone well. If the waves are so high that you might lose sight of swimmers, you may have to stand in your lifeguard stand. You will learn about potentially hazardous conditions specific to your facility during orientation.

Underwater hazards

Be aware of common underwater hazards:

- Holes
- Sudden drop-offs
- Submerged objects, such as rocks, trees, and underwater plants (Fig. 9-2)
- Bottom conditions (sand, rock, silt, weeds, and mud)
- Slope of the bottom and water depth

Fig. 9-2

If possible, underwater hazards should be removed. If hazards cannot be removed, swimming areas should be positioned away from them. Floating buoys may mark underwater hazards to warn patrons of their danger.

Pier formations

Piers in the water are often used for different activities (Fig. 9-3A-D).

With piers you should—

- Ensure that floating piers and rafts are anchored securely.
- Be aware of blind spots in your surveillance caused by piers.
- Prohibit diving into water less than 9 feet deep. (Check the water depth before allowing head-first entries.)
- Prohibit swimming in diving areas.
- Know that a 1-meter diving board requires a water depth of at least $11^{1}/_{2}$ feet, that extends out at least 16 feet from the end of the board.

Fig. 9-3A "F" formation

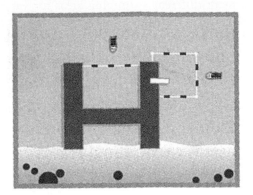

Fig. 9-3B "H" formation

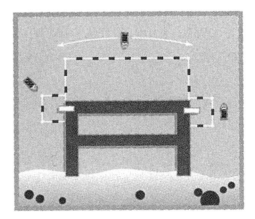

Fig. 9-3C "A" formation

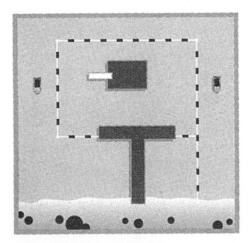

Fig. 9-3D "T" formation

Changing water conditions

Water depth and currents can affect patron safety. Heavy rainfall can make a river rise, or a long, dry period may make it too shallow for diving. When a dam releases water, the water depth above the dam drops and the river depth below the dam rises. Debris in the water or cloudi-

ness may also affect safety. Water is usually colder early in the summer and after rain. Although surface water may be warm and comfortable, water at a depth of several feet can be much colder. This condition, called a thermocline, can cause a cold-water hazard.

With changing water conditions you should—

- Warn patrons of hazards.
- Check for objects that may have washed into the area.
- Check for changes in bottom conditions and water depth.
- Alert patrons to cold water, and watch for signs of hypothermia.

Changing weather conditions

At an outdoor facility, you need to watch for changing weather conditions. Follow the emergency action plan (EAP) when severe weather threatens. The following steps may be taken when a storm approaches:

- Have a staff member track the approaching storm.
- Inform your supervisor.
- Clear patrons from swimming areas and tell them where to go.

Lightning tends to strike tall metal structures, electrical wires, and moving water. Follow the lightning guidelines in Chapter 2.

Safety checks

Frequent safety checks may be needed for changing waterfront conditions. Before opening the waterfront for the day, inspect the waterfront and equipment:

- Check bottom conditions for hazards or change in water depth.
- Inspect the shoreline for sharp objects, broken glass, rocks, and litter.
- Check the sand around lifeguard stands for objects that could injure you when you jump off the stand to make a rescue.
- Check piers for loose or protruding nails, rotting wood, and weak or frayed anchor lines.
- Make sure that all safety equipment is in the right place and in good working condition. Report any damaged or missing equipment.
- Check play structures for safety.

Patron Surveillance

Waterfronts are used for many activities, such as recreational swimming, boating, sailing, swimming lessons, canoeing, use of personal water craft, SCUBA diving, and water skiing. Waterfronts often have different zones for such activities. Having these activities go on at the same time complicates your surveillance. In addition to watching swimmers, you may have to warn people on boats, personal water craft, or water skis to stay away from the swimming area.

If waves reduce your visibility, the facility manager may suspend swimming until conditions improve. Be sure to watch the lifelines at the far end of the swimming area when you scan. Distressed swimmers may hold onto these when they become tired. At some waterfronts, buoyed lifelines mark different swimming areas for various skill levels. If you feel a patron might not be safe in an area, caution that patron or give a simple swimming test to allow the patron to stay in that area.

Make sure you know the exact area you are assigned to cover. Talk to your supervisor if your zone seems so large that your response in an emergency would take too long. Figure 9-4, A and B, shows two possible zone coverage patterns at a waterfront.

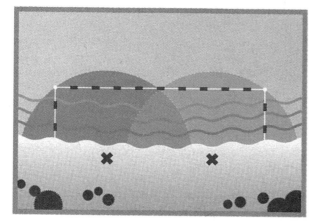

Fig. 9-4A, Two-lifeguard zone coverage

Fig. 9-4B, Three-lifeguard zone coverage

Lifeguard stations

The location of your lifeguard station must enable you to see your entire area of responsibility. You may have to move your lifeguard stand or change your position during the day to adjust for the changing sun, wind, or water conditions. Make sure you always have a clear view of the whole area and can see everyone in it (Fig. 9-5).

Rescue craft

In many facilities, lifeguards watch swimmers from rescue craft. Rescue craft typically patrol the outer edge of a swimming area (Fig. 9-6). Often you can reach someone in trouble in the water more quickly from a rescue craft.

Fig. 9-5

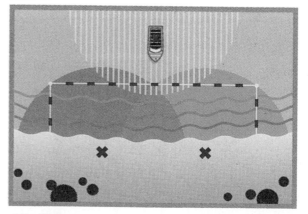

Fig. 9-6

In a small, calm area, a rescue board or a flat-bottom row-boat may be used. In rough water, a v-hull or tri-hull rowboat may be used (Fig. 9-7A). Powerboats, inflatable boats (Fig. 9-7B), and personal water craft also can be used as rescue craft. You will learn about the facility's rescue craft in your orientation.

Be sure your rescue craft is properly equipped. Inspect your equipment at the start of each shift, and tell the head lifeguard or facility manager about any damaged or missing equipment. A rescue boat should have at least the following equipment:

- Extra oars or paddles
- Several life jackets
- Rescue tube
- Anchor and line
- First aid kit
- Bailer

If stationed in a rescue craft in water with a current, you may have to row or paddle to stay in position. In rough water or a strong wind, you will need to be in good physical condition for constant rowing or paddling. Some rescue craft use a special anchor line with a quick release for

Fig. 9-7A

Fig. 9-7B

making a rescue. In some larger rescue craft, one lifeguard maintains the craft's position while a second watches the swimming area.

Make sure you are well trained in operating your facility's rescue craft before you use them for surveillance or to make a rescue. Be even more cautious with rescue craft with a motor. Take care to avoid injuring swimmers or damaging lifelines when you cross into the swimming area to make a rescue.

Patron surveillance at camps

Patron surveillance at camp waterfronts is similar to surveillance at other open-water facilities. Be aware of unique characteristics of the waterfront and swimmers' abilities. Classifying swimmers and using a buddy system and buddy board make supervision more effective.

Classification of swimmers

Camp lifeguards screen the swimming skills and abilities of participants for all aquatic activities, such as swimming and boating. This screening is done at the beginning of the camp session to determine which activities individual campers can participate in. Groups for different activities are formed based on these abilities. In some camps the swimmers also wear color-coded swim caps (Fig. 9-8) or wrist bands to help you see that they stay in their designated areas.

Fig. 9-8

Buddy system

The buddy system is used in many camps for supervising swimmers. This involves pairing off campers with equal swimming ability. In some situations with an uneven number in the group, have three campers form a triplet. The buddies must stay together in the assigned swimming area. If either buddy leaves the water for any reason, the other buddy must also leave.

Fig. 9-9

Periodically check on all swimmers with a buddy check. Two methods are commonly used:

- A lifeguard gives a signal, like a whistle blast. The buddies grasp each other's hands, raise their arms over their heads, and hold still while the lifeguards count the swimmers in each area (Fig. 9-9).
- In the other method, pairs of buddies are given numbers. A lifeguard gives a signal and then calls off numbers in order. The buddies call out when their buddy number is called.

Never depend on the buddy system as the only method of supervision. Constantly watch your area of responsibility, looking for swimmers in trouble.

Buddy boards

Some camps also use buddy boards to be sure buddies stay in their assigned area (Fig 9-10). Buddy boards are usually located by the swimming or boating area. Based on the initial screening, campers get colored tags with their names or assigned numbers. Tags are color-coded or labeled by swimming ability, such as "nonswimmer" or "beginner." Tags are kept in the "out" section of the

Fig. 9-10

buddy board when the campers are out of the swimming area. Before entering the area, campers move their tags to the "in" section and are paired with a buddy of equal swimming ability. A lifeguard or other staff stationed at the buddy board makes sure the tags are placed correctly. When campers leave the swimming or boating area, they put the tags back in the "out" section.

A tag found in the "in" section of the board after the water is cleared may mean—

- The camper forgot to move the tag to the "out" side before leaving.
- The tag was wrongly moved by another camper or a camper is playing a joke.
- A lifeguard or other staff stationed at the buddy board failed to make sure the tag was moved correctly when the camper left.
- A tag that fell off the buddy board is not in the "in" section.
- You have a missing person.

In any case, respond quickly and efficiently. Perform the buddy check one or even two more times. If you have any doubt at all about the whereabouts of the missing person, you must initiate your missing person procedure.

Emergency Preparation

Being prepared for an emergency means more than just knowing how to rescue someone in trouble. You must also know the communication system used at the facility and your role in all kinds of emergencies.

Communication

Good communication is essential at waterfronts. Communication systems may involve two-way radios, telephones, flags, megaphones, whistles, and signals with rescue equipment.

In your orientation at the facility, be sure you understand the communication methods used. In the opening safety check each day—

- Check that the telephone is working.
- Make sure change is available for using a pay phone, if needed, and that emergency numbers are posted nearby.
- Check the battery charge in all two-way radios.
- Check the charge of a battery-operated megaphone.

Emergency Action Plans

Every facility has EAPs for emergency situations (see Chapter 4). EAPs at waterfronts and camps may include additional steps because of the environment, the weather, or the size of the waterfront and its surroundings. In rural areas, it may take longer for EMS personnel to arrive than at an urban pool setting. Therefore, the waterfront's EAP should cover this longer response time.

In a park, other staff may be included in the EAP, such as park rangers, game wardens, or marine safety officers. All team members need to practice their role in EAPs. Although others may help you, you and other lifeguards still have primary responsibility for managing aquatic emergencies.

Rescue Skills

At a waterfront, you still use the rescue skills described in the earlier chapters, along with new skills in this chapter. The American Red Cross recommends using a rescue tube rather than a rescue buoy and provides training using rescue tubes. If you are required to use a rescue buoy, however, practice with that equipment in in-service training. Many waterfronts also use rescue craft and rescue boards. Practice with all equipment used at your facility.

Entries

At most waterfronts, you can use the compact jump or stride jump entries (see Chapter 5). These work well for entering the water from a pier.

Run-and-swim entry

To enter the water from a gradually sloping shoreline, use the run-and-swim entry:

1. Hold your tube and hold the excess line in one hand with the strap over your shoulder and run into the water, lifting your knees high to avoid falling (Fig. 9-11A).

Fig. 9-11A

2. When you can no longer run, drop the tube to your side, lean forward, and start swimming (Fig. 9-11B-C). *Do not dive or plunge head-first into the water; this could result in a serious head, neck, or back injury.*

Fig. 9-11B

Fig. 9-11C

Rescue approaches

The best way to swim to the victim is with a modified crawl or breaststroke. Keep the rescue tube under your armpits or torso, and swim toward the victim with your head up. Keep the rescue tube in control at all times.

Lifeguarding Tip: *If the rescue tube slips out from under your arms or torso while you are swimming to the victim, let it trail behind you. Slow down and reposition the tube before contacting the victim.*

Removal from water

To remove a victim from the water at a pier, use the same method described in Chapter 5—two-person removal from the water using a backboard. On a sloping shoreline, help someone out of the water with either the walking assist or the beach drag.

Walking assist

Use the walking assist to help a conscious victim walk out of shallow water:

1. Place one of the victim's arms around your neck and across your shoulder.

2. Grasp the wrist of the arm across your shoulder and wrap your free arm around the victim's back or waist to provide support.

3. Hold the victim firmly and help him or her walk out of the water (Fig. 9-12).

Fig. 9-12

Beach drag

On a sloping beach, the beach drag is a safe, easy way to remove someone who is unconscious or who cannot walk from the water. Do not use this technique if you suspect the victim may have a head, neck, or back injury.

1. Stand behind the victim and grasp him or her under the armpits, supporting the victim's head as much as possible with your forearms. Let the rescue tube trail behind you (Fig 9-13 A-B).

2. Walk backward and drag the victim to the shore.

3. Remove the victim completely from the water, or at least get his or her head and shoulders out of the water.

4. For an unconscious victim or a victim in shock, position the victim on the beach with the head pointing toward the water. This allows better drainage of fluids and also elevates the victim's feet as advised for shock.

Fig. 9-13A

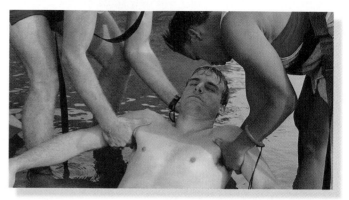

Fig. 9-13B

Surface dives

Surface dives enable you to submerge to moderate depths to search for a submerged victim. There are two kinds of surface dives: the feet-first surface dive and the head-first surface dive.

Feet-first surface dive

To perform a feet-first surface dive during a deep-water line search (a searching pattern that is discussed later), follow this sequence:

1. When the lifeguard leading the search gives the command, position your body vertically and press down with your hands and kick strongly to raise your body out of the water (Fig. 9-14A).

2. Take a breath with your arms at your sides and let your body sink underwater. Keep your legs straight and together with your toes pointed (Fig. 9-14B).

3. As your downward momentum slows, turn your palms outward and sweep your hands and arms upward (Fig. 9-14C). Repeat this arm movement until you are deep enough.

4. When you are deep enough, tuck your body and roll to a horizontal position (Fig. 9-14D).

5. Extend your arms and legs and swim underwater (Fig. 9-14E).

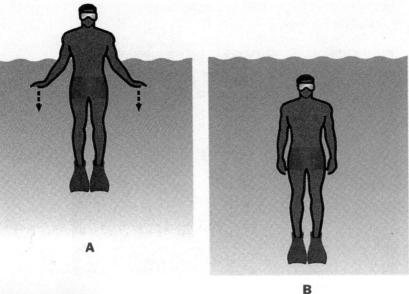

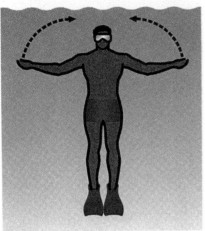

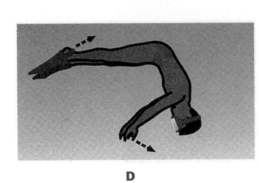

Fig. 9-14A-E

Head-first surface dive

To perform a head-first surface dive during a line search:

1. When the lead lifeguard gives the command, gain momentum with a glide or swimmer's stroke, take a breath, plunge one arm downward, and bend at the hips (Fig. 9-15A). Tuck your chin to your chest.

2. Bring the other arm down alongside the extended arm (Fig. 9-15B).

3. Press your palms up and lift your legs up in the air so that the weight of your legs helps the descent. Your body should be fully extended, streamlined, and almost vertical (Fig. 9-15C).

4. The weight of your legs and forward momentum may take you deep enough without further movement. But if necessary, kick and stroke your arms (pulling them back to the thighs) to get deeper (Fig. 9-15D). Then level out and swim forward underwater.

Fig. 9-15A

Fig. 9-15B

Fig. 9-15C

Fig. 9-15D

Caring for head, neck, and back injuries

You may have to modify how you provide care for a person with a head, neck, or back injury if waves or currents are moving the water. In water with waves, move the victim to calmer water, if possible. A pier or raft may reduce the waves. If there is no barrier from the waves, have other rescuers form a "wall" with their bodies to block the waves.

In water with a current, point the victim's head up into the current once the victim is face-up. The victim's body will become aligned with the current, minimizing the possibility of additional injury from the moving water. Your orientation and in-service training will cover the specific conditions at your facility and teach you how to adapt the head, neck, or back injury management procedures you learned in Chapter 8.

Caring for head, neck, or back injury in extremely shallow water

If you find a victim facedown in extremely shallow water (less than 2 feet), modify the head-splint technique as follows:

1. Approach the victim from the side and move the arms slowly and carefully into position. Grasp the victim's right arm with your right hand and the left arm with your left hand and trap the victim's head between the arms (Fig. 9-16A).

2. After the head is trapped between the arms, begin to roll the victim toward you.

3. While you roll the victim's head, step from the victim's side toward the victim's head and turn the victim face-up (Fig. 9-16B).

4. Lower your arm on the victim's side that is closest to you so that the victim's arms go over the top of your arm as you step toward the victim's head. You will now be positioned above and to the rear of the victim's head (Fig. 9-16C).

Lifeguarding Tip: Maintain arm pressure against the victim's head during this maneuver.

5. Hold the victim in this position.

6. Comfort the victim and monitor airway, breathing, and circulation (ABCs) until EMS personnel arrive and take over.

Fig. 9-16A

Fig. 9-16B

Fig. 9-16C

Lifeguarding Tip: If the victim is not breathing or shows no signs of circulation, immediately remove the victim from the water while maintaining in-line stabilization. Provide emergency care.

The rescue board

At some waterfronts, you will use a rescue board to patrol the outer boundaries of a swimming area. A rescue board

may also be kept by the lifeguard stand ready for emergency use. If your facility uses a rescue board, learn how to paddle quickly and maneuver it in all conditions. Wind, currents, and waves can affect how the board handles. Practice often to keep your skills sharp. Keep the board clean of suntan lotion and body oils, which can make it slippery.

To use a rescue board—

1. Hold onto the sides about midboard as you enter the water.

2. When the water is knee-deep, lay the rescue board on the water and push it forward alongside you (Fig. 9-17A). Climb on just behind the middle and lie down (Fig. 9-17B).

3. Paddle a few strokes, then bring yourself to a kneeling position so that you can effectively paddle and keep the victim in sight (Fig. 9-17C).

4. When patrolling on a rescue board, sit or kneel on it for better visibility.

Fig. 9-17A

Fig. 9-17B

Fig. 9-17C

To approach the victim on a rescue board—

1. In calm water, point the bow (front end) of the rescue board toward the victim.

2. From a kneeling position, paddle with a butterfly arm stroke.

3. Keep your head up and keep the victim in sight.

4. In rough water or high winds, adjust the angle of approach as needed.

To rescue a distressed swimmer with a rescue board—

1. Approach the victim from the side.

2. Grasp the victim's wrist and slide off the rescue board on the opposite side (Fig. 9-18A).

3. Help the victim reach his or her arms across the rescue board. Encourage the victim to relax and be calm (Fig. 9-18B).

4. Hold the rescue board stable and help the victim onto it (Fig. 9-18C).

5. Tell the victim to lie on his or her stomach facing the bow. Make sure that the bow is not underwater (Fig. 9-18D).

6. Kick to turn the board toward shore. Carefully climb onto the board from the back with your chest between the victim's legs. Be careful not to tip the rescue board, and keep your legs in the water for stability (Fig. 9-18E).

7. Paddle the rescue board to shore (Fig. 9-18F).

8. Help the victim off the board and onto shore with a walking assist.

Fig. 9-18A

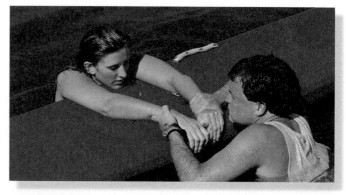

Fig. 9-18B

Fig. 9-18C

Fig. 9-18D

Fig. 9-18E

Fig. 9-18F

To rescue someone who is unconscious or cannot climb onto the rescue board—

1. Approach the victim from the side. Position the board so that the victim is slightly forward of the middle of the board.

2. Grasp the victim's hand or wrist and slide off the board on the opposite side, flipping the rescue board over toward you (Fig. 9-19A-B). You are now holding the victim's arm across the board with the victim's chest and armpits against the far edge of the board.

Lifeguarding Tip: Make sure the victim's armpits are along the edges of the board.

3. Grasp the far edge of the rescue board with your other hand (Fig. 9-19C).

4. Kneel on the edge of the rescue board using your body weight to flip the board toward you, catching the victim's head as the board comes down (Fig. 9-19D).

Lifeguarding Tip: Use caution when flipping the board to ensure that the victim's armpits and not the upper arms, remain along the edge of the board during the flip.

5. Position the victim lying down lengthwise in the middle of the board with the head toward the bow (Fig. 9-19E).

6. Kick to turn the board toward shore. Carefully climb onto the board from the back with your chest between the victim's legs. Be careful not to tip the rescue board, and keep your legs in the water for stability (Fig. 9-19F).

7. Paddle the rescue board to shore (Fig 9-19G).

8. Help the victim to safety with the walking assist or beach drag.

If you cannot get the victim onto the rescue board, use the board for flotation and hold the victim face-up to breathe. Call for help and move toward shore as best you can.

Fig. 9-19A

Fig. 9-19B

Fig. 9-19C

Fig. 9-19D

Fig. 9-19E

Fig. 9-19F

Fig. 9-19G

Using water craft for rescues

If your facility uses water craft for rescues, practice until you are skilled in managing them in all rescue situations and all weather conditions. Your facility must train you in the use of its water craft. Following are basic guidelines for using water craft:

1. Extend an oar to the victim, and pull him or her to the stern (rear) of the craft. It is the most stable area to hold onto (Fig 9-20).

2. If the victim cannot hold the oar or equipment, move the stern close to the victim. Pull the victim to the stern by the wrist or hand (Fig. 9-21).

3. Have the victim hang onto the stern as you move to safety.

4. If you need to bring the victim onto the craft because the water is very cold or the victim is fatigued, help the victim over the stern (Fig. 9-22).

When using a motorized water craft, follow these principles:

1. Always approach the victim from downwind and downstream.

2. Shut off the engine about three boat-lengths from the victim, and coast or paddle to the victim.

3. Bring the victim on board before restarting the engine.

Fig. 9-20

Fig. 9-21

Fig. 9-22

Fig. 9-23

Kayaks

Kayaking has become increasingly popular in recent years. Kayaks are used for recreation, touring, competition, sport, and as rescue craft at some waterfront facilities.

Advances in technology and the growing interest in kayaking has led to a wide variety of kayak designs, shapes, and sizes. The kayak is a unique type of craft that requires specialized skills, distinctive from those needed for other small craft. Because of this, if your facility uses kayaks, your facility manager or head lifeguard will provide you with in-service training in operational skills (boat handling and paddling) and rescue techniques to assist people who may need help in the water.

Special Situations and Skills

Sightings and cross bearings

When a drowning victim submerges, you need to swim or paddle to his or her last seen position. Take a sighting or a cross bearing to keep track of where the victim went under.

To take a **sighting**—

- Note where the victim went underwater.
- Line up this place with an object on the far shore, such as a tree, building, or anything identifiable (Fig 9-23).
- Note the victim's distance from the shore along that line.

Fig. 9-24

With two lifeguards, a **cross bearing** can be used:

- Both lifeguards take a sighting from two different angles on the spot where the victim was last seen (Fig. 9-24).
- Other people can help out as spotters from the shore.
- Both lifeguards swim toward the victim along their sight lines.
- Both lifeguards check spotters on shore for directions. Spotters communicate with megaphones, whistles, or hand signals.
- The point where the two sight lines cross is the approximate location where the victim went down.

Missing person procedure

All waterfronts have procedures for locating a missing person. All staff should be trained in these procedures. Time is critical. The "missing person" reported may be a child who just wandered off and cannot be found by the parent, but because the person may be in the water, take every missing person report seriously.

If the missing person is not found immediately, additional support may be needed from other EMS personnel. Continue your search until EMS personnel arrive on the scene to assist with the search. The EMS response can be canceled if the victim is found and does not need medical assistance.

The facility's EAP for a missing person search may be similar to the following:

Lifeguarding Tip: During all missing person procedures, one person is in charge of the search to avoid confusion and wasted time. This may be the head lifeguard or facility manager.

- Use a pre-determined signal that alerts all staff that a person is missing. Lifeguards clear the swimming areas and report to the designated area.
- All staff report immediately to the designated location. The person who reported the person missing gives a detailed description of the person and waits there to identify the person.
- If there is a public address system, an announcement is made describing the missing person. Follow facility policy whether to describe a missing child. Ask everyone to stay calm, and ask for volunteers if needed. Tell the missing person to report to the main lifeguard area. Often the person does not know someone reported him or her missing.
- One lifeguard is the lookout above the water level on a pier, raft, or water craft with rescue equipment.
- All other lifeguards search the swimming area, starting where the missing person was last seen. Look under piers, and rafts and in other dangerous locations.
- Adult volunteers can help search shallow areas, but only lifeguards search beyond chest-deep water.
- Other staff check the bathrooms, showers, locker rooms, and other areas.
- At a camp, staff quickly check the missing person's cabin or tent and other areas.
- At a camp, all campers may be moved to a central location to do a count. Lifeguards continue to search the entire waterfront until every person has been accounted for or until EMS personnel take over.
- At parks, staff may search playgrounds, campsites, and wooded areas. Park rangers, maintenance people, and volunteers may help while lifeguards search the water areas.

Searching shallow-water areas

To search water areas no more than chest deep where the bottom cannot be seen:

- A lifeguard oversees the search.
- Adult volunteers and staff link their arms and hold hands to form a line in the water. Shorter people should be in the shallower water (Fig. 9-25).
- The whole line slowly moves together across the area, starting where the missing person was last seen (Fig. 9-26).

Fig. 9-25

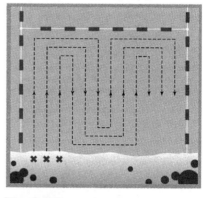

Fig. 9-26

- As the line moves forward, searchers sweep their feet across the bottom with each step. If there is a current, walk downstream.
- Only trained lifeguards should search deeper areas.

Deep-water line search

The deep-water line search is used in water greater than chest deep.

- Several lifeguards wearing masks and fins form a straight line an arm's length from each other (Fig. 9-27).
- One lifeguard is the lookout above the water level on a pier, raft, or water craft with rescue equipment.
- On command from the lead lifeguard, all lifeguards do the same surface dive (feet-first or head-first) to the bottom and swim forward a set number of strokes—usually three. If the water is murky, searchers check the

Fig. 9-27

bottom by sweeping their hands back and forth in front of them, making sure to cover the entire area. Try to avoid disturbing silt and dirt on the bottom, making the water even cloudier. Do not miss any areas on the bottom when you dive and resurface.

- Return to the surface as straight up as possible.
- The line reforms at the position of the person farthest back. The lead lifeguard accounts for all searchers, reforms the line, and backs up the line one body length. On command, the team dives again.
- Repeat this procedure until the entire area has been searched in one direction (Fig. 9-28).
- Repeat the line pattern at a 90-degree angle to the first search pattern.
- If the missing person is not found, expand the search to nearby areas. Consider whether currents may have moved the victim.
- Continue to search until the person is found or emergency personnel take over.
- If lifeguards find the victim underwater, two lifeguards should approach the victim from opposite sides. Both lifeguards grasp the victim under the armpit and return the victim to the surface. Both lifeguards should maintain their hold on the victim and swim the victim to safety, keeping the victim on his or her back, with his or her face out of the water.

Fig. 9-28

Equalizing pressure underwater

When you descend into deep water, the pressure may cause you pain or injury if you do not equalize it. Usually you feel the pressure in your ears first. Equalize the pressure early and often. If you cannot equalize the pressure because of a head cold or sinus problem, return to the surface rather than risk an injury. To relieve ear pressure—

1. Place your thumb and finger on the nosepiece of your mask.

2. Pinch your nose and try to exhale.

3. Repeat this as needed to relieve more ear pressure. If your ears hurt, do not attempt to go deeper until you successfully equalize the pressure.

4. As you descend, the mask squeezes your face because of the increased pressure. To relieve the squeezing, exhale a small amount of air through your nose into the mask.

Mask and fins

A mask and fins may be used in an underwater search for a missing swimmer. Use only good equipment that fits well.

Mask

A mask is made up of soft, flexible rubber or silicone, with nontinted, tempered safety glass and a head strap that can easily be adjusted. Some masks have additional features such as molded nosepieces or purge valves. With any design, proper fit is the primary concern.

To check that a mask fits properly—

1. Place the mask against your face without using the strap. Keep your hair out of the way.

2. Inhale slightly through your nose to make a slight suction inside the mask. This suction should keep the mask in place without being held. A good fit keeps water from leaking into the mask.

3. Adjust the strap so that the mask is comfortable. If it is too tight, the mask may not seal properly.

4. Try the mask in the water. If it leaks a little, tighten the strap. If it continues to leak, check it again with suction. You may need to try a different size.

5. To prevent mask fogging, rub saliva on the inside of the face plate, and rinse the mask before you put it on. Commercial defoggers also can be used.

Fins

Fins give you more speed and let you cover greater distances with less effort. A good fit is important for efficient movement. The fin's blades come in different sizes. Larger fins are faster but require more strength. Choose fins that match your ability.

Wetting your feet and fins first makes it easier to put them on. Do not pull on the heels or straps of the fins, which can break or tear. Push your foot into the fin, and then slide the heel or strap up over your heel.

A modified flutter kick is usually best when wearing fins. Use a kicking action that is deeper and slower, with a little more knee bend, than your usual flutter kick. It is easier to swim underwater using your legs only. Keep your arms relaxed at your side. In murky water, hold your arms in front of you for protection.

Entering the water with mask and fins

Once you are proficient with mask and fins, you can learn how to enter the water safely wearing your equipment. Enter from a height of less than 3 feet with a stride jump. Never enter head-first wearing mask and fins.

To do a stride jump with mask and fins—

1. Put one hand over the mask to hold it in place.
2. Keep your elbow close to your chest.
3. Make sure no swimmers or other objects are below you.
4. Step out with a long stride over the water, but do not lean forward (Fig. 9-29).
5. As you enter the water, the fins slow your downward motion.
6. Swim with your arms at your side and your face in the water.

Fig. 9-29

Searching for a missing SCUBA diver

All underwater searches for a SCUBA diver should be conducted by trained search and rescue SCUBA personnel. The EAP for your facility may give you an assisting role, however, including one or more of these responsibilities:

1. Find out where the diver was last seen, or look for bubbles.
2. Check other areas, such as the parking lot or equipment storage area.
3. Use a sighting or cross-bearing to keep track of the spot where bubbles or the diver was last seen.

Cold water

A serious concern at many waterfront facilities is the sudden entry of someone into cold water. Cold water is 70 degrees F (21 degrees C) or colder. As a general rule, if the water feels cold, consider it cold. Sudden entry into cold water usually occurs if a person accidentally falls in or intentionally enters the water without proper protection. A person may be swimming underwater and enter a thermocline. In any case, cold water can have a serious effect on the person and on the lifeguard making the rescue. The person can become unconscious and drown.

Sudden entry into cold water can cause the following reactions:

- A gasp reflex, a sudden involuntary attempt to "catch one's breath." If the victim's face is underwater, the person may inhale water into the lungs.
- If the person's face is not underwater, he or she may begin to hyperventilate. This can lead to unconsciousness and the risk of breathing in water.
- An increased heart rate and blood pressure can cause a heart attack.
- A victim who remains in the cold water may develop hypothermia, which can cause unconsciousness.

In some ways, cold water can be beneficial and may increase a person's chances of survival:

- In cold water, body temperature begins to drop almost as soon as the person enters the water. Swallowing water accelerates this cooling.
- As the core temperature drops, body functions slow almost to a standstill, and the person requires very little oxygen.
- Any oxygen left in the blood is diverted to the brain and heart to maintain minimal functioning of these vital organs.

Because of this, victims have been successfully resuscitated after being submerged in cold water for an extended period.

Rescues in cold water

Locate and remove a victim from cold water as quickly as possible. Because you too will be affected by cold water, try to make the rescue without entering the water if possible. Extend your rescue tube to reach the victim.

If you must enter the water, take your rescue tube with a towline attached. A line-and-reel may be used, which is a heavy piece of rope or cord attached to rescue equipment to tow you and the victim to safety. Wear body protection such as a wetsuit.

When the victim is out of the water, assess his or her condition. Victims who have been submerged in cold water may still be alive even with—

- Decreased or undetectable pulse rate.
- No detectable breathing.
- Bluish skin that is cold to the touch.
- Muscle rigidity.

Begin rescue breathing or CPR as needed and give first aid for hypothermia as soon as possible. Call EMS immediately. The sooner the victim receives professional medical care, the better the chances are for survival.

Putting it All Together

When lifeguarding at a waterfront, adapt your surveillance techniques and rescue methods for the specific conditions. You may use additional equipment at waterfronts. The more you practice these techniques and use this equipment, the better prepared you are for waterfront emergencies.

in review...

Circle the letter of the best answer or answers.

1. If wave action reduces your visibility, you may have to—
    a. Ask for additional lifeguards.
    b. Move your lifeguard stand into the water.
    c. Post a sign warning swimmers of possible danger.
    d. Suspend swimming until conditions improve.

2. Potential hazards at a waterfront include—
    a. Underwater obstructions.
    b. Good water quality and clarity.
    c. Plants and animals in the water.
    d. Currents.

3. Which of the following entries are useful when entering the water from a shoreline?
    a. Compact jump
    b. Ease-in entry
    c. Run-and-swim entry
    d. Stride jump

4. When using a rescue board to rescue a distressed swimmer, approach the swimmer from—
    a. Behind.
    b. The front.
    c. The side.
    d. Below.

5. The buddy system at camp waterfronts helps to ensure that—
    a. Each camper has a friend for the day.
    b. Each camper always wears a colored tag.
    c. No camper is alone in the water at any time.
    d. Campers teach each other to swim.

6. To rescue a distressed swimmer when using a rowboat, carefully approach the swimmer so that he or she can grasp the boat at the—
    a. Stern.
    b. Bow.
    c. Side.
    d. Gunwale.

7. When performing a shallow-water line search, searchers—
    a. Wear mask and fins.
    b. Search in water about chest deep or less.
    c. Link arms and form a line.
    d. Walk upstream if there is a current.

8. Sudden immersion in cold water can cause the following reactions:
    a. Increase in heart rate
    b. Increase in blood pressure
    c. A gasp reflex
    d. Decrease in breathing rate

Circle True or False

9. A buddy check is a swim test that one camper gives to the other.

    True   False

10. The beach drag is a safe, easy way to bring an unconscious victim out of the water.

    True   False

11. In a deep-water line search, the searchers sweep their hands back and forth in front of them along the bottom, making sure to cover the entire area.

    True   False

12. The rescue tube and rescue board are equipment used at a waterfront.

    True   False

chapter 10

waterpark
lifeguarding

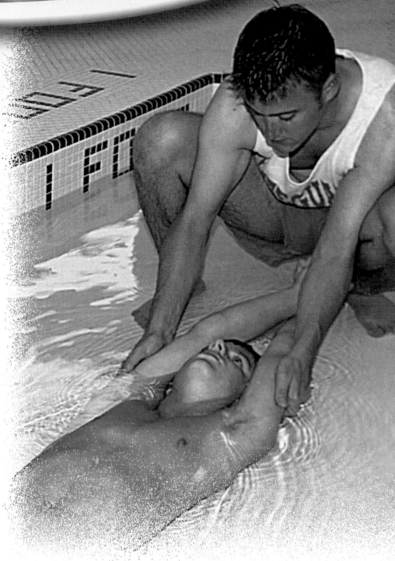

Waterparks are aquatic theme parks with attractions, such as wave pools (Fig. 10-1), speed slides, and winding rivers. Lifeguarding at a waterpark is a challenging and rewarding experience. The lifeguarding skills described in previous chapters also are used in waterparks, along with the new skills and information in this chapter. As at any facility, you need orientation and in-service training at the waterpark where you work.

Fig. 10-1

Interacting With the Public

Lifeguarding at a waterpark may be different from lifeguarding at a pool in several ways:

- More patrons are present at a time.
- More patrons are first-time visitors and not familiar with attractions.
- More kinds of attractions and play structures are present.
- More lifeguards and support staff are present.
- Lifeguards make more frequent patron water assists.
- A larger percentage of patrons are nonswimmers. Some patrons think of a waterpark like an amusement park and do not realize they need swimming skills.

A combination of these factors present at the same time can lead to difficulties. A near-drowning may occur when patrons with little swimming ability enter the water for the first time and are not familiar with an attraction.

Waterpark lifeguards frequently interact with children and adults. You may be responsible for—

- Watching children.
- Helping children and parents understand the rules.
- Enforcing rules in a fair and friendly way.
- Staying calm if a patron becomes upset.

- Helping a lost child or parent find his or her family.

When a patron needs help, be ready to respond:

- Some patrons need help when they enter or exit an attraction. Some have trouble getting their balance if they fall off an inner tube or are hit by a wave.

- Some people do not ride all the way to the bottom of a slide.

- Patrons who repeatedly break rules on attractions or cause trouble with other patrons or staff should be prohibited from using the attraction. They may act this way because of alcohol or other drugs. Keep an eye out for risky behavior and for signs of misuse of alcohol or other drugs. If a problem happens, call your supervisor immediately.

- When having a good time, some patrons may try to do more than they are able to do. They may think they know more about an attraction than they actually do, or they may simply just get excited. Keep a positive tone when you help them. Enforce the rules fairly for all.

Injury Prevention

Strategies for injury prevention, communication, patron surveillance, and facility surveillance are discussed in earlier chapters. These are used with only slight modifications in waterparks.

Rules and regulations

Rules and regulations are posted for patron safety. Some waterparks also have signs in other languages, and some have recorded messages.

- Sometimes patrons must be at least a certain height to use an attraction (Fig. 10-2). For example, on a waterslide patrons must be at least 6 inches taller than the depth of a shallow catch pool. A catch pool is a small pool at the end of a slide where patrons enter water deep enough to cushion their landing.

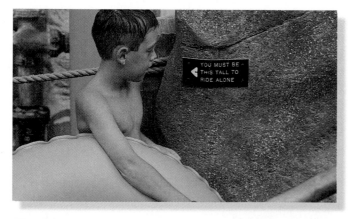

Fig. 10-2

- Children over a certain height or age are not allowed in some areas designated for small children for safety reasons.

- Warning signs tell the water depth in a catch pool. Some catch pools are shallow and patrons can stand up, but others are very deep. Patrons used to a shallow catch pool can be caught off guard in a deep catch pool.

Safety checks

Use the facility's form for doing safety checks (Fig. 10-3). Check all areas open to the public. Test ride all attractions before opening the facility.

Fig. 10-3

Following are typical items on a safety checklist:

For the whole facility:

- Slipping or tripping hazards on walkways
- Sharp objects or objects sticking out
- Loose handrails or guard rails
- Blocked or locked fire exits
- Blocked walkways or paths
- Doors to nonpublic areas locked
- Equipment or chemicals stored in locked areas
- All first aid supplies present
- First aid station clean
- Restroom and public facilities clean

For each attraction:

- Visual check or test:
  - Rafts, tubes, or sleds
  - Light signals
  - Public address (PA) system

- Telephones
- Two-way radios
- Water quality
- Water flow
- Water level
- Water temperature
- Safety equipment in proper operating condition and location:
  - Rescue tubes
  - Resuscitation masks
  - First aid kit
  - Automated External Defibrillator (AED)
  - Oxygen delivery system
  - Backboard
  - Lifejackets

Tell your supervisor about any damaged equipment so that it can be repaired or replaced. Any conditions that could be hazardous should be fixed before the facility opens. If you cannot correct a problem yourself, tell your supervisor immediately.

Lifeguard rotation

After you do safety and equipment checks, be in your assigned position on time. Your supervisor may have you move from one station to another during your shift. You may rotate through different attractions or different positions at the same attraction. Usually you rotate positions every 30 to 45 minutes to help you stay alert.

Lifeguard rotations are usually based on—

- Locations of stations.
- Type of station (sitting or standing).
- The need to be in the water at some stations.
- The number of patrons using the attraction.

Patron Surveillance

How you do patron surveillance in a waterpark is similar to what you do at other pools. You adapt your techniques for the specific attractions, however. Follow three general principles:

- Watch patrons as they enter and exit an attraction.
  - Dispatch patrons safely on a ride at the set intervals. Dispatching is the method of informing patrons when it is safe to proceed on a ride.
- Keep patrons in view as long as possible.
  - On some attractions, this is a problem. You might be able to see only the beginning or end of a long water slide. Caves, enclosed tubes, bridges, buildings, and

other structures may keep you from seeing patrons at all times. Do your best. When a patron goes out of sight behind something, watch to make sure he or she emerges safely on the other side.

- Some play equipment has special risks.
  - Structures that patrons sit or climb on or swim over or under pose hazards. Supervise carefully. A patron who falls off a mat, raft, or tube may be injured or pose a hazard to someone else.

Winding rivers

In a winding river, water flows in a long circular or twisting path through a waterpark (Fig. 10-4). Patrons float along slowly on inner tubes. Lifeguards may be stationed at the entrance and exit and at other positions with overlapping zones.

Fig. 10-4

Common rules for winding rivers follow:

- Enter and exit the winding river only at designated places.
- No jumping or diving into the water.
- Stay in tubes at all times.
- No walking or swimming in the winding river.
- No stacking of tubes.
- Only one patron allowed per tube, except for an adult holding a small child. *The child should be wearing a U.S. Coast Guard-approved life jacket, in case the adult tips over.*

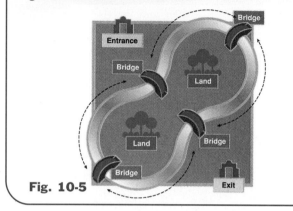

PATRON SURVEILLANCE AT WATERPARKS ACTIVITY

Directions: Determine the positioning of lifeguard stations and area of responsibility (zones) for lifeguards in the following winding river layout. Your instructor will provide you with the number of lifeguards available.

Fig. 10-5

Water slides

Water slides are long, winding slides, usually made of fiberglass or concrete (Fig. 10-6). Water is pumped down the slide from the top to the catch pool. Some slides are in enclosed tubes, and others are open.

- On some slides, patrons ride on an inner tube, raft, or mat. On other slides, they do not use riding equipment.
- Do not let patrons stop or slow down or form a chain of riders. In most slides, only one person is allowed on an inner tube or a raft. In some slides, two or more people can go together on a special tube or raft.

Fig. 10-6

- On an inner tube or raft, the rider goes feet-first in a sitting position (Fig. 10-7). If no equipment is used, the rider goes face-up and feet-first.

Fig. 10-7

The lifeguard at the top of a slide may do several things:

- Tell patrons how to ride down the slide.
- Help patrons with the equipment.
- Check that patrons are tall enough to use the slide. You may use a measuring pole or line on a wall to check their height.
- Dispatch riders at proper intervals to keep them from colliding on the slide.
- Wait longer before dispatching the next rider after lighter riders, who travel slower than heavier riders.

The lifeguard at the bottom of a slide in the catch pool has these duties:

- Supervise riders on the slide and help them get out of the water.
- Watch riders exit the slide into the catch pool.
- Watch for and help riders who may be caught in a hydraulic (Fig 10-8). (A hydraulic is a strong downward flow in the catch pool that can knock a person off balance or hold a small person or nonswimmer under water.)

Fig. 10-8

- Make sure the patrons exit from the catch pool quickly and do not cross in front of any slide when getting out of the catch pool.

At some very long slides, a lifeguard in the middle of the slide watches and helps riders.

- Riders may need help in the middle of a slide. Riders may stop, slow down, or stand up on the slide. They can be injured doing this.
- Riders may lose their mat, tube, or raft and have trouble getting down the slide.
- Riders may hit their heads on the side of the slide.

Other common guidelines for water slides include—

- No swimsuits or shorts with metal rivets, buttons, or fasteners.
- No eyeglasses or sunglasses on the slide.
- No running, standing, kneeling, rotating, or tumbling on slides, and no stopping in flumes or tunnels.

Drop-off slides

A drop-off slide ends with a drop of several feet into the catch pool (Fig. 10-9). Patrons may not realize the depth of the catch pool and need help. Point out the signs that show the water depth. A swim test may be required.

Paula Panton, Water Safety Products

Fig. 10-9

If you are supervising a drop-off slide, make sure—

- Riders sit or lie in a feet-first position.
- Each rider has moved out of the catch pool before dispatching the next.

Speed slides

A speed slide is straight and steep. It may have small hills or rises (Fig. 10-10). It usually has a runout to slow patrons to a stop in water several inches deep.

If you are stationed at the top of a speed slide—

- Let only one rider down the slide at a time.

Fig. 10-10

- The riding position is feet-first, lying on the back, with legs crossed at the ankles and arms crossed over the chest. This position is faster and reduces the risk of injury.
- Do not send a rider until the previous rider has left the runout or the catch pool and the lifeguard at the bottom signals for the next rider.
  - If you can see the lifeguard at the bottom, a hand signal and a whistle may be used.
  - If you cannot see the lifeguard at the bottom, a mechanical signal may be used.
- Enforce facility rules like—
  - No life jackets allowed (they may cause a rider to be caught or hung up).
  - No eyeglasses, sunglasses, or goggles.

If you are stationed at the bottom of a speed slide—

- Help patrons, if needed, from the runout or catch pool (Fig. 10-11). (Some may be disoriented or frightened from the ride.)

Fig. 10-11

Free-fall slides

A free-fall slide has a nearly vertical drop that provides a sensation of falling. It is like a speed slide with a steeper angle (Fig. 10-12).

Paula Panton, Water Safety Products

Fig. 10-12

Lifeguarding responsibilities for a free-fall slide are like those for speed slides.

At the top, give patrons specific directions:

- Riders in line must stand back away from the slide.
- Riders must wait for your signal to start. Signal only when you are sure that the previous rider has left the runout.
- Riders should lie flat, with ankles crossed and arms crossed over the chest.
- Riders must not sit up until they come to a complete stop.

Riders who do not follow these directions can be injured and may have—

- Friction burns on the legs and arms.
- Bumps and bruises if the rider sits forward and tumbles down the slide.
- Head, neck, or back injuries, broken bones, or sprains if the rider tumbles or twists down the slide.

Wave pools

Wave pools are popular attractions. Most produce waves of various heights, intervals, and patterns.

- Wave pools vary in size, shape, and depth (Fig. 10-13).

Fig. 10-13

- At one end is the head wall, where a mechanical system creates the waves.
- Lifeguards may be on the head wall for a better view of the wave pool (Fig. 10-14).

Fig. 10-14

- Many pools have a cycle such as 10 minutes on and 10 minutes off. The times may vary. When waves are present, stand to have a better view of patrons. When the waves are off, you may be allowed to sit, but keep scanning. Lifeguards rotate positions when the waves are off. Lifeguards are often stationed at various places around or in the pool.

Wave pools have special guidelines:

- As in other pools, the number of lifeguards depends on the size and shape of the pool and how many people are in the water, as well as local and state health codes (Fig. 10-15A-B).

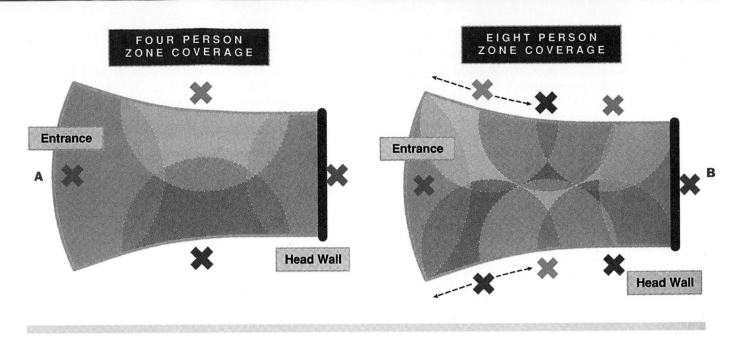

Fig. 10-15A-B

- Lifeguard chairs often have an emergency stop button to turn off waves in an emergency before you perform a rescue (Fig. 10-16). The emergency action plan should tell how lifeguards cover all zones while one is performing a rescue.

Fig. 10-16

- Patrons often go to where the waves break because of the excitement. But inexperienced swimmers can be knocked over or carried into deeper water by the waves. Most wave pool rescues take place where the waves break.

- Patrons must enter the pool only at the shallow end. Do not let patrons dive into the waves. Keep the areas around ladders and railings clear so that patrons can exit from the pool quickly.

- If the waterpark has inner tubes or inflatable rafts for the wave pool, watch for inexperienced swimmers falling off their tube in deep water. When there are many inner tubes in the water, it is difficult for you to see everyone and the bottom. In a very crowded pool, someone who falls off an inner tube or raft may have trouble coming up for air if inner tubes or rafts block the surface.

- Someone who is hit by an inflatable raft may be knocked down and hit the bottom and get into trouble. Change your scanning technique if you need to. Move to a different position to eliminate any blind spots, and watch carefully in high-risk situations.

- Some wave pools have special activities like surfing at certain times. If some people are riding surfboards or boogie boards in the wave pool, other patrons should stay out of the pool because of the hazard.

Kiddie areas

Many waterparks have shallow pools for small children. Often these have play equipment like slides, fountains, inflatable play equipment, and climbing structures (Fig. 10-17). Enforce the rules fairly and consistently, such as height and age requirements. These rules help ensure everyone's safety. Special lifeguard concerns include—

Fig. 10-17

- Older children may be too large for some structures, or they may be too rough to be around small children.
- Children often get lost. Ask adults to supervise their children at all times.
- Watch out for small children using the pool as a bathroom. The facility should have a procedure for handling this situation, following local health department guidelines.
- Children usually do not watch out for too much sun. If a child is becoming sunburned, tell the child's parents or guardian immediately.

Special attractions

Some deep-water pools have activities like specialty slides, diving platforms, cable swings, or hand-over-hand structures like ropes, nets, and rings (Fig. 10-18). These attractions may make surveillance difficult. Orientation and in-service training will include these attractions. Special lifeguard concerns include—

Fig. 10-18

- Carefully watch both the water below and activities overhead.
- With a rope or cable swing over a deep-water pool, let only one person swing at a time. Do not allow horseplay on platforms. Patrons might not know how deep the water is, and nonswimmers can get in trouble in deep water.
- Do not allow diving in water less than 9 feet deep.
- "Lily pads" are flat, floating structures tethered to the bottom of the pool. Patrons walk from one lily pad to another, holding on an overhead rope (Fig. 10-19). Watch for overcrowding and horseplay.

Paula Panton, Water Safety Products

Fig. 10-19

- A rapids ride is a rough-water attraction that is like white-water rafting. Patrons ride in inner tubes or rafts and should be in the same body position as on water slides. Lifeguards may be positioned at the top, the bottom, and in between to watch all parts of the ride (Fig. 10-20). Lifeguarding responsibilities are similar to those for water slides and winding rivers.
- On some slides the rider sits on a plastic sled. Enforce the height requirement for this attraction. The lifeguard at the top of the slide starts sledders with a mechanical control. The lifeguard at the bottom watches for a sled flipping over or colliding. A signaling system is used to start riders. Lifeguarding responsibilities are similar to those at other slides.

Fig. 10-20

Emergency Preparation

All waterpark staff may be on the safety team along with lifeguards. EMS personnel, concessionaires, equipment rental personnel, admissions personnel, security guards, and maintenance personnel are all on the team. In an emergency, staff may help control crowds, meet arriving EMS personnel, clear attractions, make announcements on the public address (PA) system, and help with first aid.

Different waterparks have different amounts and types of training. A staff member may have several different roles in a small facility or one main role in a large facility. Everyone must know his or her role in the emergency action plan (EAPs). Other factors to consider in an EAP for waterparks include—

- Stopping the waves or slide dispatch.
  - At a wave pool, push the emergency stop button to turn the waves off.
  - If you are stationed at the top of an attraction, do not start any more riders.
  - Use set whistle signals, hand signals, flags, or lights to communicate with other lifeguards.
- If another lifeguard is making a rescue, make sure that lifeguard's zone is covered.
  - In deep water, all lifeguards stand in their chairs and adjust their zone coverage to cover the zone of the lifeguard making the rescue.
  - In shallow water, a nearby lifeguard moves to cover both his or her own zone and the rescuing lifeguard's zone.

Rescue Skills

Lifeguards at waterparks use the same rescue skills as lifeguards anywhere else. You may use these additional skills:

- Run-and-swim
- Simple assist
- Walking assist
- Front-and-back carry
- Beach drag
- Caring for head, neck, and back injuries in special situations

Entries

Compact jump

Use the compact jump to enter water at least 5 feet deep from a height of at least 3 feet. Chapter 5 gives a detailed description.

Lifeguarding Tip: In a wave pool, time your jump to land on the crest (top) of a wave.

Run-and-swim entry

To enter the water from a gradual slope, such as a wave pool, use the run-and-swim entry:

1. Hold your tube and hold the excess line in one hand with the strap over your shoulder and run into the water, lifting your knees high to avoid falling.

2. When you can no longer run, put the rescue tube across your chest, lean forward, and start swimming

(Fig. 10-21). *Do not dive or plunge head-first into the water; this could result in a serious head, neck, or back injury.*

Fig. 10-21

Assists

Assists are the most common help you will give waterpark patrons. Assists include—

- Helping patrons enter and exit an attraction.
- Helping patrons in or out of inner tubes or rafts.
- Helping a tired swimmer reach shallow water or a ladder.
- Helping a patron who is stuck in a slide or becomes frightened:
  - You may have to climb up a slide to reach a patron, or catch the person coming down.
  - Talk to the person to help calm him or her.
  - If a rescue is needed instead of an assist, start the EAP.

Simple assist

In some lifeguarding positions, you are stationed in the water, such as standing in a catch pool. A simple assist may be as easy as helping a person to his or her feet. You can do this in two ways:

- Keeping your rescue tube between you and the person who needs help, reach across the tube and grasp the person at the armpit to help the person maintain his or her balance (Fig. 10-22A).

Fig. 10-22A

- If the person is underwater, grasp him or her under the armpits with both hands and help him or her stand up (Fig. 10-22B).

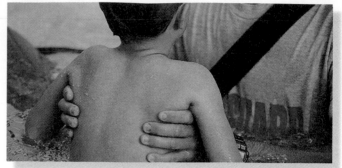

Fig. 10-22B

Removal from water

You can use three techniques to help someone out of shallow water:

1. Walking assist

2. Front-and-back carry

3. Beach drag

Walking assist

Use a walking assist to help a conscious victim walk out of the water on a gradual slope, such as the entrance of a wave pool. This technique is described in Chapter 6.

Front-and-back carry

Use the front-and-back carry if the person is unconscious or cannot get out of the water without help. Do not use this method if you suspect the victim has a head, neck, or back injury.

1. Call a second lifeguard for help.

2. From behind the victim, reach under the armpits. Grasp the victim's right wrist with your right hand and left wrist with your left hand. Cross the victim's arms across his or her chest (Fig. 10-23A).

Fig. 10-23A

3. The second rescuer stands between the victim's legs, facing away from the victim. This rescuer bends down and grasps the victim under the knees (Fig. 10-23B).

Fig. 10-23B

Fig. 10-24A

4. On signal, both of you lift the victim and carry him or her out of the water (Fig. 10-23C).

Fig. 10-23C

Fig. 10-24B

Beach drag

On a gradual slope, the beach drag is a safe, easy way to remove someone who is unconscious or who cannot walk from the water. Do not use this technique if you suspect the victim may have a head, neck, or back injury.

1. Stand behind the victim and grasp him or her under the armpits, supporting the victim's head as much as possible with your forearms. Let the rescue tube trail behind you.

2. Walk backward and drag the victim toward the shore (Fig. 10-24A-B).

3. Remove the victim completely from the water, or at least get his or her head and shoulders out of the water.

4. For an unconscious victim or a victim in shock, position the victim on the beach with the head pointing toward the water. This allows better drainage of fluids and also elevates the victim's feet higher as advised for shock.

Rescue assist by a second lifeguard

In a wave pool or deep-water attraction, you may need help from another lifeguard when making a rescue.

1. If the victim is much larger than you, signal for another lifeguard to help. Do not attempt the rescue alone.

2. The second lifeguard signals before entering the water and then swims to the front of the victim while you remain in the back with your tube across your chest (Fig. 10-25).

Fig. 10-25

3. At the count of three, the second lifeguard pushes his or her rescue tube to the victim's chest while you reach under the victim's armpits and grasp that tube, squeezing the victim between the two rescue tubes.

4. When the victim calms down, the second rescuer swims forward, pushing the victim and you to the wall or to shallow water.

Caring For Head, Neck, and Back Injuries

Use the techniques for head, neck, and back injuries that were described in Chapter 8. In-line stabilization and backboarding are more difficult to perform in some waterpark attractions. Moving water and confined spaces can cause problems. In your orientation and in-service training, you will learn and practice the in-line stabilization and backboarding procedures used at your facility.

Extremely shallow water technique

If you find a victim face-down in extremely shallow water (less than 2 feet), modify the head-splint technique this way:

1. Approach the victim from the side and move his or her arms slowly and carefully into position. Grasp the victim's right arm with your right hand and the left arm with your left hand, and trap the victim's head between the arms (Fig. 10-26A).

2. After the head is trapped between the arms, begin to roll the victim toward you.

3. While you roll the victim to a face-up position, step from the victim's side toward the victim's head and turn the victim 180 degrees (Fig. 10-26B).

Fig. 10-26A

Fig. 10-26B

4. Lower your arm on the victim's side that is closest to you so that the victim's arms go over the top of your arm as you step toward the victim's head. You are now positioned above and to the rear of the victim's head (Fig. 10-26C).

Fig. 10-26C

Lifeguarding Tip: *Maintain arm pressure against the victim's head during this maneuver.*

Winding rivers

- Head, neck, or back injuries are rare in winding rivers, but they may still occur. Injuries may result from rough horseplay in inner tubes or jumping or diving into the water. The special problem in winding rivers is that the current can pull or move the victim.

- The EAP may include signaling another lifeguard to turn off the flow of water.

- Ask other lifeguards or patrons to help you keep objects and people from floating into you as you support the victim.

- Do not let the current press sideways on the victim or force the victim into a wall. This would twist the victim's body. Keep the victim's head pointed upstream into the current. This position also reduces the splashing of water on the victim's face. When you have performed in-line stabilization and the victim is face-up (Fig. 10-27A), slowly turn the victim so that the current pulls his or her legs around to point downstream (Fig. 10-27B).

- Place the victim on a backboard and follow the facility's immobilization procedure.

Fig. 10-27A

Fig. 10-27B

Catch pools

The water in a catch pool moves with more force than in a winding river. An eddy or hydraulic makes it difficult to hold the victim still (Fig. 10-28).

Fig. 10-28

- If you suspect a person has a head, neck, or back injury in a catch pool, immediately signal other lifeguards to stop sending down riders.
- If possible, someone should stop the flow of water.
- After you perform in-line stabilization with the victim face-up, move the victim to the calmest water in the catch pool. If there is only one slide, the calmest water is usually at the center of the catch pool (Fig. 10-29A). If several slides empty into the same catch pool, calmer water is usually between two slides (Fig. 10-29B).
- Place the victim on a backboard and follow the facility's immobilization procedure.

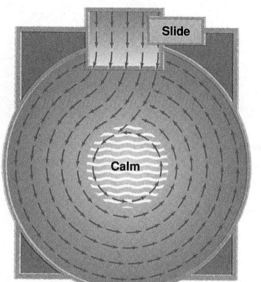

Fig. 10-29A

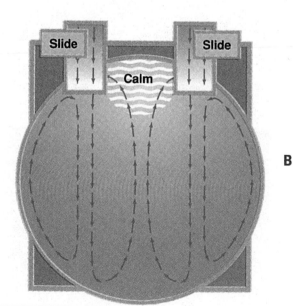

Fig. 10-29B

Speed slide

The narrow space of a speed slide causes an extra problem for a head, neck, or back injury. A head, neck, or back injury may happen if the victim's body twists or turns the wrong way. Someone may strike his or her head on the side of the slide. A patron may sit up and tumble down the slide. Backboarding can be a challenge because the water in the slide is only 2 or 3 inches deep and does not help support the victim. The procedure requires several lifeguards:

1. The first rescuer performs in-line stabilization to the head and neck while the victim is on the slide (Fig. 10-30A).

2. Other rescuers lift the victim above the slide so that the backboard may be slid in place (Fig. 10-30B).

Fig. 10-30A

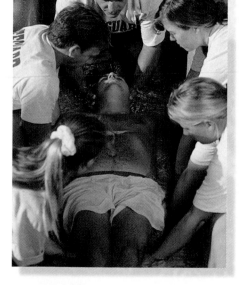

Fig. 10-30B

3. Slide the backboard beneath the victim from the feet to the head (Fig. 10-30C).

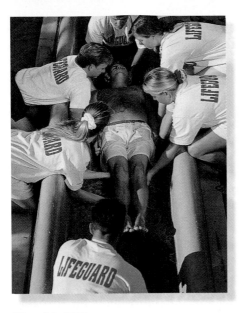

Fig. 10-30C

4. Lower the victim onto the backboard (Fig. 10-30D).

Fig. 10-30D

5. After the straps and head immobilizer are secured, lift the backboard out of the slide (Fig. 10-30E).

Fig. 10-30E

Putting it All Together

Waterpark facilities are popular but create new challenges for lifeguards. Lifeguards use many of the same skills as at other facilities, as described in earlier chapters. But lifeguards must adapt some skills for the moving water and tight spaces of various attractions.

in review...

Circle the letter of the best answer or answers.

1. A small pool at the end of a slide where patrons enter the water to cushion their landing is called—
   a. A catch pool.
   b. A landing pool.
   c. A wading pool.
   d. A plunge pool.

2. The safety team at a large waterpark includes—
   a. Lifeguards.
   b. Security guards.
   c. Admissions personnel.
   d. Concessionaires.

3. Which of the following is a method of starting patrons safely on a ride?
   a. Sequencing
   b. Stationing
   c. Ride interval
   d. Dispatch

4. While making a rescue, if you are entering the water from a height, such as a head wall or a lifeguard chair, you must perform a—
   a. Stride jump.
   b. Run-and-swim.
   c. Compact jump.
   d. Ease in.

5. When patrons drop into the water from a drop-off slide, they frequently need assistance because—
   a. The height of the drop makes them dizzy.
   b. They become disoriented.
   c. They do not realize that the catch pool is deep.
   d. The water in the catch pool is moving.

6. When caring for a victim with a head, neck, or back injury in a winding river, once the victim is in a face-up position, the victim's head should be—
   a. Pointing upstream.
   b. Pointing downstream.
   c. Pointing perpendicular to the current.
   d. Pointing diagonally to the current.

7. Which of the following is the first step in caring for a victim of head, neck, or back injury in a speed slide or free-fall slide once the water at the attraction has been turned off and all dispatch has stopped?
   a. Lifeguard applies in-line stabilization to the victim's head and neck while the victim is still in the slide.
   b. Lifeguards place their hands beneath the victim with his or her arms and elbows inside the slide.
   c. Lifeguard rolls the victim onto one side.
   d. Lifeguards place the victim on a backboard.

in review...

8. Most wave pool rescues occur—
   a. At the sides or wall.
   b. In deep water.
   c. Where the waves break.
   d. At the entrance to the wave pool.

Circle True or False.

9. When performing a simple assist in a shallow catch pool, keep the rescue tube between you and the person you are helping.

   True   False

10. In a catch pool with only one slide, the calmest water for managing a head, neck, or back injury is usually on the far side away from the slide.

    True   False

11. The walking assist is a quick and effective way to get an unconscious victim out of a wave pool.

    True   False

12. As part of a safety check, lifeguards should ride all attractions before opening the facility.

    True   False

chapter 11

AED
automated external defibrillation

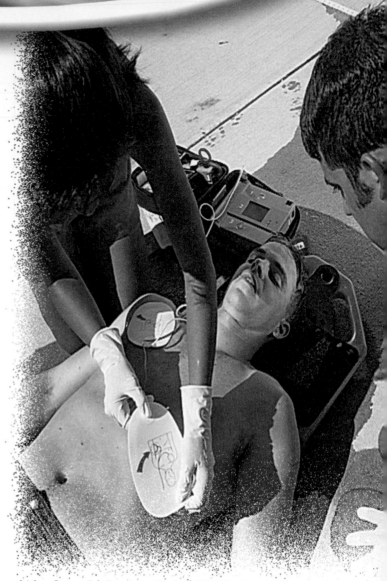

A man suddenly goes limp while swimming laps. He is passive and floating on the surface. You promptly recognize the emergency, activate the EAP, and enter the water. Once the victim is removed from the water, you determine that he is unconscious and shows no signs of circulation. Your facility has an AED. How would you respond? Do you know what to do?

Each year, approximately 250,000 Americans die as a result of sudden cardiac arrest (SCA). Most of these arrests occur away from a hospital, where the care needed to correct the cardiac arrest condition is not readily available. CPR, started promptly, can help by keeping oxygen flowing to the brain and other vital organs. However, in most cases CPR by itself is insufficient to correct the underlying heart problem.

Automated external defibrillators (AEDs) are needed to correct the problem (Fig. 11-1). AEDs provide an electri-

Fig. 11-1

cal shock to the heart, called defibrillation. The sooner the shock is administered, the greater the likelihood of the victim's survival. Lifeguards typically respond to emergencies first and need to know how to quickly assess victims and be prepared to use an AED in cases of cardiac arrest. Using an AED promptly increases the chance of survival among cardiac arrest victims. This chapter covers the basic principles of how AEDs work and how to use them.

When the Heart Fails

Any damage to the heart, caused by either disease or injury, can disrupt the heart's electrical system. This disruption can result in an abnormal heart rhythm that can stop circulation. The two most common abnormal rhythms that are present initially in cardiac arrest victims are ventricular fibrillation (V-fib) and ventricular tachycardia (V-tach). V-fib is a state of totally disorganized electrical activity in the heart. It results in fibrillation, or quivering, of the ventricles. This fibrillation is not adequate for the ventricles to pump blood. Consequently, there are no signs of circulation, including no pulse.

V-tach refers to a very rapid contraction in the ventricles of the heart. Though there is electrical activity resulting in a regular rhythm, the rate is often so fast that the heart is unable to pump blood properly. As with V-fib, when blood flow is severely impaired, there will be no signs of circulation, including no pulse.

Defibrillation

In many cases, V-fib and V-tach rhythms can be corrected by early defibrillation. Delivering an electrical shock with an AED disrupts abnormal electrical activity, such as V-fib and V-tach, long enough to allow the heart to spontaneously develop an effective rhythm on its own. If not interrupted, electrical activity will eventually cease, a condition called asystole. Asystole cannot be corrected by defibrillation. Remember that you will not be able to tell what, if any, rhythm the heart is in by feeling for signs of circulation, including a pulse. CPR, begun immediately and continued until defibrillation, helps maintain a low level of circulation in the body until abnormal rhythms are corrected by defibrillation.

AEDs and the Cardiac Chain of Survival

There are four steps in the cardiac chain of survival. Each step plays an important part in the victim's survival.

1. Early recognition and early access. The sooner you recognize the problem and call 9-1-1 or the local emergency number, the better.

2. Early CPR. Begin CPR immediately and continue until an AED arrives on the scene and is ready to use.

3. Early Defibrillation. Each minute that defibrillation is delayed reduces the chance of survival by about 10 percent.

4. Early Advanced Life Support. This is given by trained medical personnel who provide further care and transport to medical facilities.

Using an AED

In a situation involving cardiac arrest, an AED should be put to use as soon as it is available and safe to do so. CPR in progress must be stopped once the AED is applied. Most AEDs can be operated by following these simple steps:

1. Confirm cardiac arrest. Check for consciousness and the absence of signs of circulation, including a pulse.

2. Turn on the AED.

3. Wipe the victim's chest dry. Apply the pads to the victim's chest. Place one pad on the victim's upper right chest and the other pad on the victim's lower left side. Plug the electrode cable into the AED.

4. Let the AED analyze the heart rhythm (or push the button marked "analyze").

5. Deliver a shock by pushing the button if indicated and prompted by the AED after ensuring that no one is touching the victim and that there are no hazards present (such as standing puddles of water).

Whether you are the primary or secondary rescuer, you should always check the victim for signs of circulation, including the absence of a pulse, before turning on the AED.

In some cases, the heart will not require defibrillation. Recheck for signs of circulation, including a pulse. Leave the AED attached to the victim. If the victim has no signs of circulation, resume CPR. If there are signs of circulation but no breathing, give rescue breaths with a resuscitation mask or bag-valve-mask (BVM).

AED Precautions

- Do not touch the victim while defibrillating. You or someone else could get shocked.

- Do not use alcohol to wipe the victim's chest dry. Alcohol is flammable.

- Do not use an AED in a moving vehicle. Movement may affect the analysis.

- Do not use an AED on a victim who is in contact with water. Move victims away from puddles of water or swimming pools or out of the rain before defibrillating.

- Do not use an AED on a victim lying on a conductive surface. Conductive surfaces, such as sheet metal or metal bleachers, may transfer the shock to others.

- Do not use an AED on an infant or a child under age 8 or under 55 pounds. AEDs do not have the capability to adjust to the low-energy settings needed for infants and children. Local protocols may differ on this and should be followed.

- Do not use an AED on a victim wearing a nitroglycerin patch or other patch. Remove any patches from the chest before attaching the device.

- Do not touch the victim while the AED is analyzing. Touching or moving the victim may affect the analysis.

- Do not defibrillate someone around flammable materials, such as gasoline or free-flowing oxygen.

- Do not use a cellular phone or radio within 6 feet of the AED. This may interrupt analysis.

Sample AED Protocol

Check for Signs of Circulation (No Pulse)

If no pulse……..Do CPR until the AED is attached.

Analyze Rhythm

If shock advised……Defibrillate.

Analyze Rhythm

If shock advised……Defibrillate.

Sample AED Protocol—continued

Analyze Rhythm

If shock advised.......Defibrillate.

Recheck for Signs of Circulation (No Pulse)

If no pulse......Do 1 minute of CPR and then recheck for signs of circulation (no pulse).

If still no pulse.......Repeat analysis and set of 3 shocks.

Recheck for Signs of Circulation (No Pulse)

If no pulse.......Do 1 minute of CPR and then recheck for signs of circulation (no pulse).

If still no pulse......Repeat analysis and set of 3 shocks as indicated.

Recheck for Signs of Circulation (No Pulse)

If still no pulse.....Continue CPR and prepare for transport by EMS personnel.

Note: As long as there are no signs of circulation and the AED still indicates a need to shock, continue repeating sets of 3 shocks to the maximum your local protocols allow, with 1 minute of CPR between each set. Be thoroughly familiar with your local protocols, which may vary from this table.

AEDs—Special Situations

Some situations require rescuers to pay special attention when using an AED. It is important that lifeguards be familiar with these situations and be able to respond appropriately.

AEDs around water

When using an AED at an aquatic facility, be sure that the victim is placed a backboard and moved away from the pool or water's edge. Be sure that there are no standing puddles of water around the victim or near where the AED is being used. Dry the victim's chest thoroughly using towels or gauze pads. Water on the skin can cause electrode problems and decrease the effectiveness of the shock delivered to the heart. Proceed to use the defibrillator as in any situation. If you are outdoors and it is raining, move the victim to shelter first before using the AED, unless moving the victim would significantly delay care.

AEDs and pacemakers

Peoples whose hearts are weak and not able to generate an electrical impulse may have a pacemaker implanted. These small devices may be located in the area below the right collarbone. If visible, or you know that the victim has a pacemaker or other implantable device, do not place the pads directly over the pacemaker. This may interfere with the delivery of the shock. Adjust pad placement and continue to follow local protocols.

AEDs and nitroglycerin patches

People who have a history of cardiac problems may use nitroglycerin patches (Nitropatch®) (Fig 11-2).

These patches are usually placed on the chest. If you find a patch on the victim's chest, remove it with a gloved hand. Although patches do not interfere with defibrillation, time may be wasted attempting to identify the type of patch. Any medication patches should be removed from the victim's chest prior to using the AED.

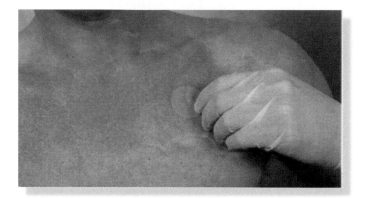

Fig. 11-2

Putting it All Together

Automated external defibrillators (AEDs) save lives. To defibrillate a victim of cardiac arrest using an AED, follow these basic steps:

1. Confirm cardiac arrest (no signs of circulation/pulse).

2. Turn on the AED.

3. Wipe the chest dry, apply the pads to the victim's chest, and plug the electrode cable into the AED.

4. Let the AED analyze the heart rhythm (or push the button marked "analyze").

5. Deliver a shock if one is indicated after ensuring that no one is touching the victim and that there are no hazards present (such as standing puddles of water).

Be sure to follow local protocols when using an AED. They are relatively easy to operate and generally require minimal training and retraining. When using an AED at an aquatic facility, be sure that the victim is placed on a backboard, and moved away from the pool or water's edge.

in review...

Circle the letter of the best answer or answers.

1. **An electrical shock delivered to the heart to correct certain life-threatening heart rhythms is called—**
   a. Asystole.
   b. Diastole.
   c. Fibrillation.
   d. Defibrillation.

2. **It is important to stand clear before using an AED to deliver a shock because—**
   a. The pads could become loose.
   b. The AED will not work unless you stand clear.
   c. You could be injured by the shock.
   d. The AED will not deliver the correct shock to the victim.

3. **An abnormal but organized heart rhythm causing rapid contraction of the ventricles that results in the inability of the heart to pump adequate blood is—**
   a. Ventricular fibrillation.
   b. Ventricular tachycardia.
   c. Asystole.
   d. Normal sinus rhythm.

4. **After confirming that a victim shows no signs of circulation (pulse), the next step is—**
   a. Turn on the AED.
   b. Wipe the chest dry, apply the pads to the victim's chest, and plug the electrode cable into the AED.
   c. Let the AED analyze the heart rhythm (or push the button marked "analyze").
   d. Deliver a shock if one is indicated after ensuring that no one is touching the victim and that there are no hazards present (such as standing puddles of water).

5. **When using an AED at an aquatic facility—**
   a. Dry the victim's chest thoroughly using towels.
   b. Move the victim to shelter after removing him or her from the water.
   c. Place the victim on a backboard.
   d. Make sure no standing puddles are near the victim or the AED.

Circle True or False.

6. **If you find a nitroglycerin patch on a victim's chest, remove it with a gloved hand before using an AED.**

   True   False

7. **The pads of an AED should be placed on the upper right side of the victim's chest and the lower left side of the victim's chest.**

   True   False

8. **AEDs are hard to operate and are not reliable in most cases.**

   True   False

Using an AED

Complete Steps 1-8, Primary Survey Skill Sheet, pages 62-63
Remember: Always follow basic precautions to prevent disease transmission.

9. If the victim shows no signs of circulation (pulse)—
   Turn on the AED.

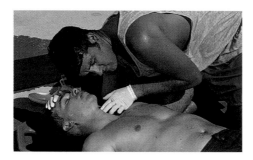

10. Prepare to use the AED.

    ■ Wipe the victim's chest dry.

    Lifeguarding Tip: *Thoroughly wipe the chest dry prior to applying the pads. Water on the skin of the chest can cause electrode problems and decrease the effectiveness of the shock delivered to the heart.*

    ■ Attach the pads to the victim.

    ■ Place one pad on the victim's upper right chest and the other pad on the victim's lower left side.

    ■ Plug the electrode cable into the AED.

    Lifeguarding Tip: *If the victim was removed from the water, be sure that there are no standing puddles of water around the victim or near where the AED is being used.*

11. Let the AED analyze the victim's heart rhythm (or push the "analyze" button).

    ■ Make sure no one is touching the victim.

    ■ Say, "EVERYONE STAND CLEAR."

    Lifeguarding Tip: *Be sure no one is touching or moving the victim while the AED is analyzing or shocking the heart rhythm. The primary rescuer should be sure that everyone is clear prior to the analyzing or shocking of the heart rhythm.*

12. Deliver a shock if prompted.

If the AED advises that a shock is needed—

■ Make sure that no one is touching the victim.

■ Say, "Everyone stand clear."

■ Deliver a shock when prompted by pushing the "shock" button.

■ Repeat Step 11.

OR

If the AED advises no shock is needed—

Recheck for signs of circulation (pulse).

If there are signs of circulation and NO breathing—

Give Rescue Breathing.

■ Rescue Breathing—Adult Skill Sheet, page 64

■ Rescue Breathing—Child Skill Sheet, page 65

If there are still NO signs of circulation...

Do CPR until the AED reanalyzes.

Using an AED—
CPR in progress

Complete Steps 1-8, Primary Survey Skill Sheet, pages 62-63

9. If the victim shows no signs of circulation and an AED is on the way—

   ■ Do CPR until the AED is ready to use.

   ■ Go to CPR—Adult steps 9-13 or Go to CPR—Child steps 9-13.

10. When the AED is ready to use—
    Recheck for signs of circulation.

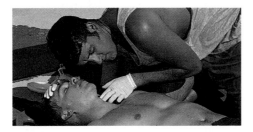

11. If the victim shows no signs of circulation (pulse)—
    Turn on the AED.

12. Prepare to use the AED.

    ■ Wipe the victim's chest dry.

    Lifeguarding Tip: *Thoroughly wipe the chest dry prior to applying the pads. Water on the skin of the chest can cause electrode problems and decrease the effectiveness of the shock delivered to the heart.*

    ■ Attach the pads to the victim.

    ■ Place one pad on the victim's upper right chest and the other pad on the victim's lower left side.

    ■ Plug the electrode cable into the AED.

Lifeguarding Tip: *If the victim was removed from the water, be sure that there are no standing puddles of water around the victim or near where the AED is being used.*

13. Let the AED analyze the victim's heart rhythm (or push the "analyze" button).

    ■ Make sure that no one is touching the victim.

    ■ Say, "EVERYONE STAND CLEAR."

Lifeguarding Tip: *Be sure no one is touching or moving the victim while the AED is analyzing or shocking the heart rhythm. The primary rescuer should be sure that everyone is clear prior to the analyzing or shocking of the heart rhythm.*

14. Deliver a shock if prompted.

If the AED advises a shock is needed—

■ Make sure no that one is touching the victim.

■ Say, "Everyone stand clear."

■ Deliver a shock when prompted by pushing the "shock" button.

■ Repeat Step 13.   OR

If the AED advises no shock is needed—

Recheck for signs of circulation (pulse).

If there are signs of circulation but NO breathing—

Give Rescue Breathing.

■ Rescue Breathing—Adult Skill Sheet, page 64
■ Rescue Breathing—Child Skill Sheet, page 65

If there are still NO signs of circulation—

Do CPR until the AED reanalyzes.

chapter 12

oxygen
administration

A 45-year-old man on the pool deck is complaining of chest pain. He says it started about 30 minutes ago as discomfort in the chest. Now the pain is severe and the man is gasping for breath. You recognize he has a serious condition. You direct another lifeguard to call 9-1-1 for assistance. While waiting for advanced medical personnel to arrive, you ask permission to give care and you help him rest quietly in the most comfortable position.

You are called to the locker room to help in a medical emergency. After surveying the scene, you find a woman lying on the locker room floor. She appears to be unconscious. You check for responsiveness and she does not respond. You have someone call 9-1-1 and continue your primary survey.

What do these situations have in common? In both situations you could use supplemental oxygen to help the person. By using supplemental oxygen along with breathing devices, you can give better care to an ill or injured person.

Breathing Barriers and Devices

Many different breathing barriers and devices may be used in aquatic settings. Which barriers and devices are used in the facility where you work depends on your area.

This chapter describes the most commonly used barriers and devices. You may use these yourself or assist other staff in using them. You do not need to wait for a barrier or device before starting to provide care. You may use these barriers and devices when they are available. Breathing barriers and devices can help you—

- Keep the victim's airway open.
- Give rescue breathing.
- Prevent disease transmission.
- Get more oxygen to the victim.

Suctioning

Sometimes injury or sudden illness results in foreign matter, such as mucus, water, or blood, collecting in the victim's airway. One method of clearing the airway is to suction it. Suctioning is the process of removing foreign matter by means of a manual (Fig. 12-1A) or mechanical (Fig. 12-1B) device. A variety of manual and mechanical devices are used to suction the airway.

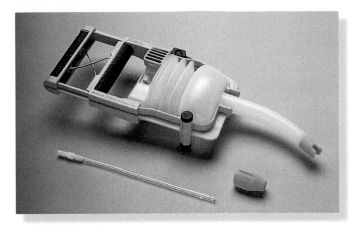

Fig. 12-1A

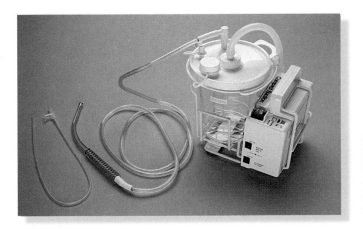

Fig. 12-1B

Manual suction devices are lightweight, compact, and relatively inexpensive. Mechanical suction devices use either battery-powered pumps or oxygen-powered aspirators and are normally found on ambulances. Attached to the end of any suction device is a suction tip. These come in various sizes and shapes. Some are flexible and others are rigid.

Airways

The tongue is the most common cause of airway obstruction in an unconscious person. Breathing devices known as oral and nasal airways can help you keep the victim's airway open.

An oropharyngeal (oral) airway is inserted into the mouth of an unconscious victim who does not have a gag reflex. A nasopharyngeal (nasal) airway is inserted into a nostril and may be used on responsive victims who need help to keep the tongue from obstructing the airway. When properly positioned, either of these airways keeps the tongue out of the back of the throat, thereby keeping the airway open. An improperly placed airway device can compress the tongue into the back of the throat, further blocking the airway.

Airways come in a variety of sizes (Fig. 12-2 A-B). The curved design fits the natural contour of the mouth, nose, and throat. Once you have positioned the device, you can use a resuscitation mask or bag-valve-mask resuscitator to ventilate a nonbreathing victim.

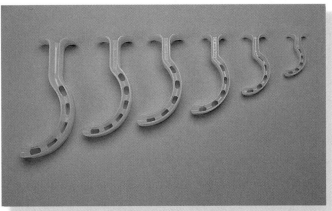

Fig. 12-2A

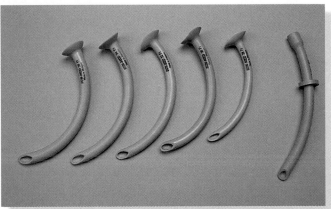

Fig. 12-2B

Resuscitation masks

Resuscitation masks are flexible devices that fit over a victim's mouth and nose (Fig.12-3). If fitted with an oxygen delivery inlet and attached to an oxygen cylinder, resuscitation masks can help you deliver more oxygen to the per-

Fig. 12-3

son than would otherwise be delivered. Resuscitation masks have several benefits:

- They get air into the victim more quickly through both the mouth and nose.
- They are easy to seal on the victim's face.
- They can be hooked up to oxygen.
- They help protect you against disease transmission when giving rescue breaths to a victim.

Be sure the mask you use has the following characteristics (Fig 12-4), or ask management for a different one:

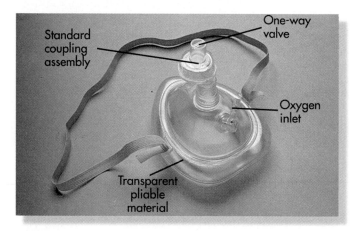

Fig. 12-4

- Is easy to assemble and use
- Is made of a transparent, pliable material that lets you make a tight seal on the victim's face to perform rescue breathing or give supplemental oxygen
- Has a one-way valve for releasing exhaled air
- Has a standard 15-mm or 22-mm coupling assembly (the size of the opening for the one-way valve)
- Has an inlet for hooking up supplemental oxygen

- Works well under different environmental conditions, such as extreme heat or cold

Bag-Valve-Mask resuscitators

A bag-valve-mask (BVM) resuscitator is a hand-held device used to get oxygen into a nonbreathing victim (12-5). It can also be used for a victim in respiratory distress. The BVM—

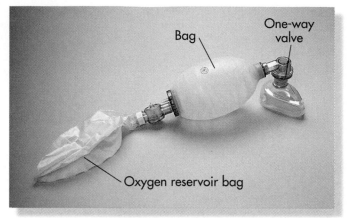

Fig. 12-5

- Protects you against disease transmission.
- Increases oxygen levels in the blood.
- Is highly effective when used by two rescuers.

Because it is necessary to maintain a tight seal on the mask, you need two rescuers to operate the BVM (one rescuer positions and seals the mask, while the other rescuer squeezes the bag).

Using a BVM—One rescuer

In the rare case you are the only rescuer on the scene and a BVM is available, you can still use the BVM. However, you may have a difficult time maintaining a tight seal and also maintaining an open airway for effective ventilation. To use the BVM by yourself:

1. Assemble the bag-valve-mask.

2. Position the mask so that it covers the victim's mouth and nose.

3. Open the airway.

4. With one hand, hold the mask with a "C-clamp" with your index finger and thumb around the mask (Fig. 12-6). Keep the airway open using your other fingers to lift the jaw. Use your knees to help hold the victim's head in this tilted position.

Using a BVM—One rescuer—continued

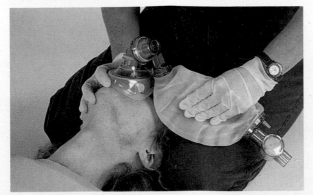

Fig. 12-6

5. With one hand, press down on the mask to maintain a tight seal and help open the victim's mouth. With your other hand, squeeze the bag slowly until the victim's chest clearly rises. You can squeeze the bag against your thigh if your hands are too small to do it with one hand.

Supplemental oxygen

About 21 percent of the air we breathe is oxygen. That is enough oxygen most of the time, but a victim who is injured or ill can benefit from getting more oxygen. Supplemental oxygen refers to oxygen given from a tank rather than from the air. Supplemental oxygen can help save the life of someone having a heart attack. It can also help other injured or ill victims.

When you breathe air from your own lungs into the victim during rescue breathing, the victim only gets about 16 percent oxygen. If you use a BVM by itself, the victim gets 21 percent oxygen—the percentage that exists in the air. But using supplemental oxygen with the BVM allows you to deliver up to 100 percent oxygen to the victim. To give supplemental oxygen, you need a supplemental oxygen delivery system:

Fig. 12-7A

Fig. 12-7B

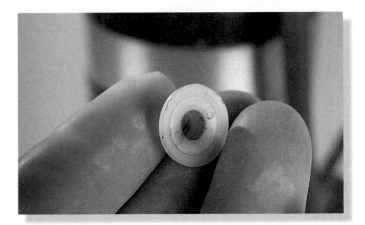

Fig. 12-7C

- An oxygen cylinder
- A pressure regulator with flowmeter
- A delivery device

Oxygen cylinder

Oxygen cylinders are marked green with a yellow diamond that says *oxygen* (Fig. 12-7A). Oxygen tanks are under high pressure and should be handled carefully. The pressure regulator lowers the pressure coming out of the tank so that the oxygen can be used safely (Fig. 12-7B). The pressure regulator also has a gauge that shows pressure in the cylinder. The gauge shows you if the cylinder is full (2,000 psi), nearly empty (200 psi), or somewhere in between. The pressure regulator must be carefully attached to the oxygen cylinder. An "O-ring" gasket makes the seal tight (Fig. 12-7C).

The flowmeter controls how fast the oxygen flows out to the victim. Oxygen flow is measured in liters per minute. The flow can be set from 1 to 25 liters per minute (1pm).

Oxygen delivery devices

Oxygen delivery devices get the oxygen from the cylinder to the victim. The resuscitation mask and the BVM can be used to deliver oxygen to victims who are breathing or not breathing. Tubing carries the oxygen from the flowmeter on the tank to the device on the victim. Some resuscitation masks have elastic straps to put over the victim's head to keep the mask in place (Fig. 12-8). If the mask does not have a strap, either you or the victim can hold it in place.

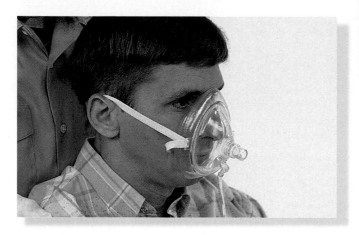

Fig. 12-8

The BVM can also be held to a breathing victim's face to allow him or her to inhale the oxygen (Fig. 12-9). A victim breathing less than 10 breaths per minute, or more than 30 per minute, should be assisted with oxygen. Squeeze the bag as the victim inhales to help deliver more oxygen.

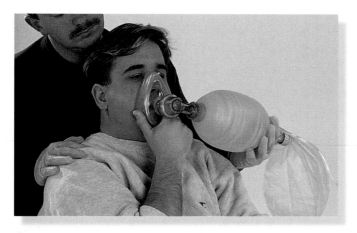

Fig. 12-9

A nasal cannula delivers oxygen to someone who is breathing (Fig. 12-10). It has two small prongs that are inserted into the nose. Nasal cannulas are not often used because they do not give as much oxygen as a resuscitation mask or BVM. These are used mostly for victims with minor breathing problems rather than for life-threatening emergencies. If a victim will not accept having a mask on his or her face, however, a nasal cannula can be used.

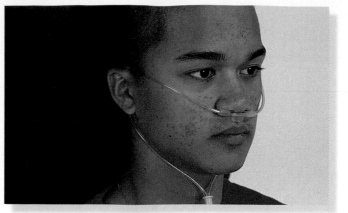

Fig. 12-10

Using a non-rebreather mask (Fig. 12-11) is the most effective method for delivering high concentrations of oxygen to conscious breathing victims. The non-rebreather mask consists of a face mask with an attached oxygen reservoir bag and a one-way valve between the mask and bag to prevent the victim's exhaled air from mixing with the oxygen in the reservoir bag. As the victim breathes, he or she inhales oxygen from the bag. Flutter valves on the side of the mask allow exhaled air to escape freely. When using the non-rebreather mask with a high flow rate of oxygen, up to 90 percent oxygen can be delivered to the victim.

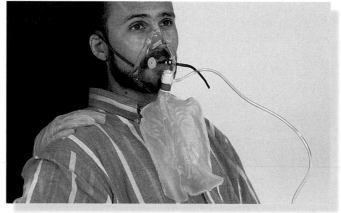

Fig. 12-11

The setting you choose on the flowmeter depends on which device you use. With a nasal cannula, set the flow rate at 1-4 1pm. With a resuscitation mask, set the rate at 6 1pm or more. With non-rebreather masks, the flow rate should not be lower than 10 lpm. Remember the general rule: *one to four and six or more.* Table 12-1 summarizes the delivery devices.

Table 12-1 *Oxygen Delivery Devices*

Device	Common flow rate	Oxygen concentration	Function
Nasal Cannula	1-4 lpm	24-36 percent	Breathing victims only
Resuscitation Mask	10+ 6+ lpm	5-55 percent	Breathing/nonbreathing victims
Non-rebreather Mask	10 lpm	90+ percent	Breathing victims only
BVM Resuscitator	10+ lpm	90 + percent	Breathing/nonbreathing victims

Oxygen-Powered resuscitators

Oxygen-powered resuscitators are another oxygen delivery device used in some settings. These are also called demand valves. They can deliver oxygen to either breathing or nonbreathing victims and work like a BVM. However, instead of using the bag to supply air, it uses pressurized oxygen. The rescuer presses a button to force oxygen into the victim's lungs. The use of the demand valve to ventilate a nonbreathing victim is commonly called positive pressure resuscitation.

The advantages of using a demand valve are giving a high concentration of oxygen (approaching 100 percent), ease of use, and protection from disease transmission. Disadvantages are a higher cost, the need for a constant source of oxygen, and rapidly using up the oxygen. In addition, giving too much oxygen can be a problem, or the device may not meet the needs of a victim in severe respiratory distress. The device should not be used to ventilate nonbreathing children or infants. Follow your local protocol for using demand valve resuscitators.

Precautions

When administrating oxygen, safety is a concern. Follow these guidelines:

- Do not use oxygen around flames or sparks. Oxygen causes fire to burn more rapidly.
- Do not stand oxygen cylinders upright unless they are well secured. If the cylinder falls, the regulator or cylinder valve could be broken.

- Do not use grease, oil, or petroleum products to lubricate the pressure regulator. This could cause an explosion.
- Always make sure that oxygen is flowing before putting the mask over the victim's face.

Clearing the airway

Vomit, blood, or anything else in the victim's mouth may block the airway. Before you give rescue breathing or oxygen, roll the victim onto his or her side and sweep the mouth clean. Alternatively, you could use a suctioning device to help clear the airway.

Putting It All Together

Breathing devices make emergency care safer, easier, and more effective. Supplemental oxygen can relieve pain and make breathing easier. Breathing devices increase the oxygen the victim gets, help get oxygen into a nonbreathing victim, and help prevent disease transmission.

Breathing devices can be used in all types of injury or illness when the victim shows signs of breathing problems. Knowing how to use these devices help you to provide more effective care until more advanced medical personnel arrive and take over.

in review...

Match each term in the first column with its appropriate definition in the second column. Write the letter of the correct definition on the line next to the term.

1. Flowmeter_____	**A** Regulates oxygen delivery in liters per minute (lpm).
2. Nasal Cannula_____	**B** Best used by two rescuers, because one rescuer may have difficulty keeping the airway open while maintaining a tight enough seal.
3. Resuscitation Mask_____	**C** Used to administer oxygen to a victim who is breathing, but has a low oxygen flow.
4. Oxygen Cylinder_____	**D** Has an internal pressure of approximately 2,000 pounds per square inch.
5. Bag-Valve-Mask (BVM) Resuscitator_____	**E** A flexible dome-shaped device that fits over the victim's nose and mouth and is used in giving rescue breathing.

Circle the letter of the best answer or answers.

6. **Which is a benefit of using a resuscitation mask to provide artificial ventilation?**
   a. It reduces the volume of air needed to expand the victim's lungs.
   b. It prevents airway obstructions caused by facial injuries.
   c. It reduces the risk of disease transmission between rescuer and victim.
   d. All of the above.

7. **When using a resuscitation mask, the best way to maintain an open airway is by—**
   a. Tilting the person's head back.
   b. Lifting the jaw upward.
   c. Keeping the person's mouth open.
   d. All of the above.

8. **A pressure regulator should not be lubricated with a petroleum product because of the danger of—**
   a. Contamination of the oxygen.
   b. An explosion.
   c. Loosening the oxygen cylinder valve.
   d. Inaccurate readings from the oxygen flowmeter.

9. **The O-ring should be placed on the oxygen cylinder—**
   a. After the regulator is in place.
   b. After you have examined the pressure regulator.
   c. After you have opened the cylinder for 1 second.
   d. After you have verified the oxygen flow.

10. **An oral airway is the correct size if it extends from the victim's—**
    a. Nose to the point of the chin.
    b. Nose tip to the earlobe.
    c. Earlobe to the corner of the mouth.
    d. Front teeth to the back of the tongue.

11. **Which step do you take when using a manual or mechanical suction device?**
    a. Keep the victim's head turned to the side.
    b. Sweep debris from the mouth before suctioning.
    c. Suction for no more than 15 seconds at a time.
    d. All of the above.

in review...

Circle True or False.

12. For a proper seal, place one rim of the resuscitation mask between the victim's lower lip and chin.

    True   False

13. A benefit of breathing devices is that the rescuer can deliver a higher concentration of oxygen to the victim than with simple rescue breathing.

    True   False

14. The oxygen delivery device should be placed over the victim's face before oxygen begins to flow from the device.

    True   False

15. A victim with a serious injury can benefit from supplemental oxygen.

    True   False

16. Oxygen should not be used around open flames or sparks.

    True   False

17. A victim should not be suctioned for more than 15 seconds at a time.

    True   False

18. A nasal airway can only be used in an unresponsive victim.

    True   False

Fill in the blanks.

19. The four items of equipment necessary for giving supplemental oxygen are—

    _____

    _____

    _____

    _____

20. The four safety precautions you should follow when administering oxygen are—

    _____

    _____

    _____

    _____

using a resuscitation mask for rescue breathing

Remember: Always follow basic precautions to prevent disease transmission.

1. Assemble the mask.

   - Attach the one-way valve to the resuscitation mask.

2. Position the mask.

   - Kneel behind the victim's head and place the rim between the lower lip and chin, and lower the resuscitation mask until it covers the victim's mouth and nose.

3. Seal the mask and open the victim's airway.

- *From the back of the victim's head—*

  - Place your thumbs on each side of the resuscitation mask.

  - Slide your fingers into position behind the angles of the victim's jawbone.

  - Apply downward pressure with your thumbs, lift the jaw, and tilt the head back to open the airway.

- *From the side of the victim's head—*

  - Kneel next to the victim. Position the resuscitation mask to cover the victim's mouth and nose.

  - Seal the resuscitation mask and open the airway.

  - Apply downward pressure, lift the jaw, and tilt the head back to open the airway.

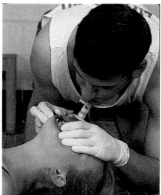

- *If you suspect the victim may have a head, neck, or back injury—*

  - Use the two-handed jaw thrust technique.

- Slide your fingers into position behind the angles of the victim's jawbone.

- Without moving the victim's head, apply downward pressure with your thumbs, and lift the jaw to open the airway.

4. Begin rescue breathing.

- Give 1 rescue breath about every 5 seconds (once about every 3 seconds for a child or infant).

- Watch the victim's chest clearly rise and fall with each rescue breath.

- Recheck for signs of circulation every minute.

oxygen delivery

Remember: Always follow basic precautions to prevent disease transmission.

1. Check the cylinder.

   - See that the label is marked oxygen.

2. Clear the valve.

   - Remove the protective covering and save the plastic gasket.

   - Open cylinder for 1 second to clear the valve.

3. Attach the pressure regulator.

   - Put the plastic gasket into the valve on top of the cylinder.

   - Check that it is marked Oxygen Pressure Regulator.

   - Place the regulator on the cylinder. Seat the three metal prongs into the valve.

   - Hand-tighten the screw until the regulator is snug.

4. Open the cylinder ONE full turn.

■ Check the pressure gauge.

■ Determine that the cylinder has enough pressure.

5. Attach the delivery device.

■ Attach the plastic tubing between the flowmeter and the delivery device.

6. Adjust the flowmeter.

■ Turn the flowmeter to the desired flow rate.

■ With a nasal cannula, set the flow rate at 1-4 1pm.

■ With a mask, set the rate at 6 1pm or more.

■ With non-rebreather masks, the flow rate should not be lower than 10 lpm.

7. Verify the oxygen flow.

■ Listen and feel for oxygen flow through the delivery device.

8. Place the delivery device mask on the victim.

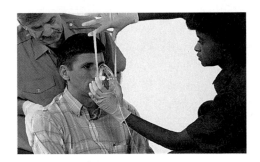

suctioning

Remember: Always follow basic precautions to prevent disease transmission.

1. Position the victim.

   - Turn the victim's head to one side.

   - If you suspect a head, neck, or back injury, roll the victim onto one side while maintaining in-line stabilization.

   - Open the mouth.

2. Sweep large debris from the mouth using your finger.

3. Measure suction tip.

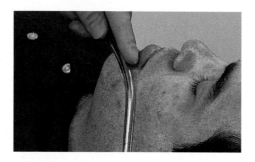

   - Measure from the victim's earlobe to the corner of the mouth.

   - Note the distance to prevent inserting the suction tip too deeply.

4. Turn on machine and test.

5. Suction the mouth.

   - Insert the suction tip into the back of the mouth.

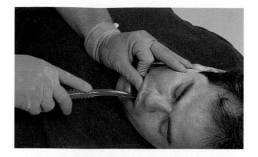

   - Apply suction as you withdraw the tip using circular motion.

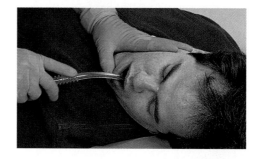

   - Suction for no longer than 15 seconds at a time.

inserting an oral airway

Remember: Always follow basic precautions to prevent disease transmission.

9. Select the proper size.

   - Measure the airway from the victim's earlobe to the corner of the mouth.

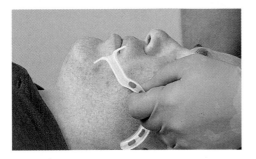

10. Open the victim's mouth.

    - Use the cross-finger technique to open the victim's mouth.

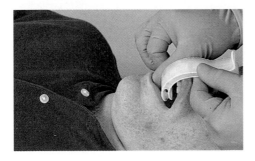

11. Insert the airway.

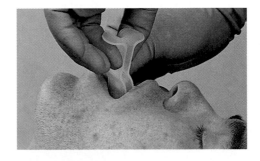

    - Insert the airway with the curved end along the roof of the mouth.

    - As the tip approaches back of the mouth, rotate it a half turn.

    - Slide the airway into the back of the throat.

12. Ensure correct placement.

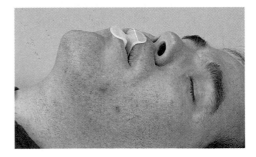

    - The flange should rest on the victim's lips.

    - If the victim begins to gag, immediately remove the airway.

inserting a nasal airway

Remember: Always follow basic precautions to prevent disease transmission.

1. Select the proper size.

   - Measure the nasal airway from the victim's earlobe to the tip of the nose. Ensure that the diameter of the airway is not larger than the nostril.

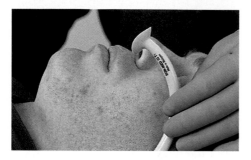

2. Lubricate the airway.

   - Use a water-soluble lubricant to lubricate the airway prior to insertion.

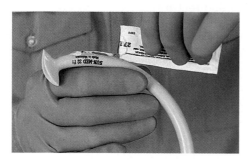

3. Insert the airway.

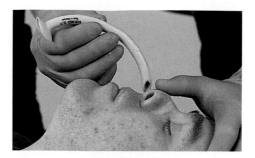

   - Insert the airway into the nostril, with the bevel toward the tissue dividing the nostrils.

   - Advance the airway gently, straight in.

   - If resistance is felt, do not force.

4. Ensure correct placement.

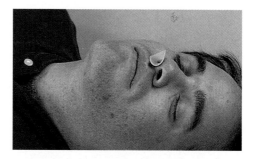

   - The flange should rest on the nose.

chapter 13

preventing
disease transmission

A man has collapsed on the pool deck. He is bleeding from the mouth and face. Vomit and blood are on the deck around him. "His face hit the deck when he fell," a bystander says. He does not appear to be breathing. How would you respond? Do you know what to do to avoid getting an infectious disease from this man, assuming he happens to have one?

Why This Training is Important

To help protect against disease transmission, you first need to understand how infections occur, how diseases are passed from one person to another, and what you can do to protect yourself and others. Infectious diseases are those you can catch from other people, animals, insects, or things that have been in contact with them. Because some infectious diseases are very serious, like hepatitis and HIV, the virus that causes AIDS, lifeguards must learn how to protect themselves and others from disease transmission. This chapter will teach you how.

OSHA

The Occupational Safety and Health Administration (OSHA) issued regulations about job exposure to germs

that can cause disease. OSHA determined that employees are at risk when they are exposed to blood or other body fluids. OSHA therefore requires employers to reduce or remove hazards from the workplace that may place employees into contact with infectious material. The guidelines prepared in this chapter help meet the goal of preventing disease transmission.

OSHA Regulations

OSHA regulations apply to employees who may be expected to come into contact with blood or other substances that could cause an infection. These regulations apply to you as a lifeguard because you are expected to give emergency care as part of your job. These guidelines help you and your employer meet the OSHA standard to prevent transmission of serious disease.

How Infections Occur

Germs

Pathogens, or germs, can cause an infection if they get into the body. Bacteria and viruses are the two most common kinds of germs found almost everywhere in our environment. Our body's own defenses can usually fight off most of these germs. When infected with a bacteria, antibiotics and other medications are often used to cure the infection. But some infectious diseases cannot be cured at all. Many of these can be deadly. That is why it is crucial to prevent the infection in the first place.

Disease-Causing Agents

Pathogen	Diseases and Conditions They Cause
Viruses	Hepatitis, measles, mumps, chicken pox, meningitis, rubella, influenza, warts, colds, herpes, shingles, HIV infection including AIDS, genital warts
Bacteria	Tetanus, meningitis, scarlet fever, strep throat, tuberculosis, gonorrhea, syphilis, chlamydia, toxic shock syndrome, Legionnaires' disease, diphtheria, food poisoning
Fungi	Athlete's foot, ringworm
Protozoa	Malaria, dysentery
Rickettsia	Typhus, Rocky Mountain spotted fever
Parasitic Worms	Abdominal pain, anemia, respiratory and cardiac problems

How Diseases Spread

You can catch a disease only if all four of these things happen:

1. A pathogen is present.

2. Enough of the pathogen is present to cause disease.

3. You are susceptible to the pathogen.

4. The pathogen gets into your body.

While you have no control over the first two requirements for disease transmission listed above, you can reduce your susceptibility to some diseases. Make sure that you have had all your immunizations and keep a healthy immune system by eating a well-balanced diet.

The fourth thing is most important, because you can do a lot to prevent germs from getting into your body. Pathogens can get into your body in four ways:

Direct contact

Direct contact (Fig. 13-1) means you directly touch another person's body fluids, such as blood. This can happen when providing first aid if you are not careful and fail to follow basic precautions to prevent disease transmission, such as not wearing gloves.

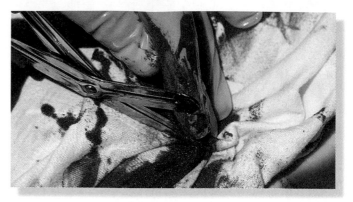

Fig. 13-1

Indirect contact

Indirect contact (Fig. 13-2) means you touch something that already came into contact with blood or other body fluids, such as saliva and vomit. This can happen if you touch soiled dressings, equipment, and work surfaces. For example, if you carelessly handle soiled dressings, you could come into contact with infected blood or other body fluids. You are not touching the victim directly, but you are touching something that has been in contact with the victim.

Fig. 13-2

Airborne

Airborne transmission (Fig. 13-3) occurs when breathing in air from an infected person's cough or sneeze.

Fig. 13-3

Vector-borne

Vector-borne transmission (Fig. 13-4) occurs when the body's skin is pierced by an infectious source, such as an animal or insect bite or sting. Lifeguards working outdoors, particularly in park environments, may choose to

Fig. 13-4

use a spray or lotion to help prevent mosquito and tick bites. Lifeguards should take care when handling sharp objects, such as needles or broken glass, which can place them at risk of injury.

Serious Communicable Diseases

The common cold is an example of a communicable disease easily passed from one person to another, but it is usually not serious. The diseases described below, however, are serious (Table 13-1). You should learn how to avoid contracting these diseases.

Herpes

Several different viruses cause herpes infections. They are very easily passed from an infected person to someone else by direct contact. The virus can stay unnoticed in the body or can cause headaches, a sore throat, or a general ill feeling. Blister-like cold sores may occur around the lips and mouth. Serious forms of herpes make sores on the face, neck, or genitals. There is no cure for most forms of herpes; you should try to avoid unprotected contact with people with active herpes.

Meningitis

Meningitis is a severe infection of the brain and spinal cord. It can be caused by either viruses or bacteria. You can get the viral form of meningitis from contaminated food or water. Meningitis can be transmitted through the air (airborne transmission) if an infected person coughs or sneezes near your face or if you come into direct contact with the person's mucus. Bacterial meningitis can be contracted when giving unprotected rescue breathing to an infected person.

Table 13-1   *How Diseases are Transmitted*

Disease	Signs and Symptoms	Mode of Transmission	Infective Material
Herpes	Sores, general ill feeling, sore throat	Direct contact	Broken skin, mucous membranes
Meningitis	Respiratory illness, sore throat, nausea, vomiting	Airborne, direct and indirect contact	Food, water, mucous membranes
Tuberculosis	Weight loss, night sweats, occasional fever, general ill feeling	Airborne	Saliva, airborne droplets
Hepatitis	Flu-like symptoms, jaundice	Direct and indirect	Blood, saliva, semen, feces, food, water, other products
HIV	Fever, night sweats, weight loss, chronic diarrhea, severe fatigue, shortness of breath, swollen lymph nodes, lesions	Direct and indirect	Blood, semen, vaginal fluid

Meningitis is more common in young children. However, adults are also at risk. Fortunately, if diagnosed and treated early, this disease can be cured. When treated early, meningitis is rarely fatal.

Tuberculosis

Tuberculosis (TB) is caused by bacteria that live in the lungs. Infection often occurs after inhaling air around an infected person, especially if the person is coughing or sneezing. Early stages of TB are often mild. People with TB may not even know that they are infected until they become seriously ill. While TB can often be cured with medications, some new kinds of TB have become resistant to drugs and are harder to cure.

Hepatitis

Hepatitis is a disease of the liver. There are many different kinds of hepatitis infections. Some infections are caused by alcohol abuse or other illnesses. Others are caused by viruses. Hepatitis A is often called infectious hepatitis and is common in children. It can be transmitted by contact with food or objects handled by an infected person. Hepatitis A usually does not have serious consequences.

Hepatitis B is a severe liver infection caused by hepatitis B virus. Hepatitis B is transmitted through sexual contact or contact with an infected person's blood or other body fluids. It is not transmitted by casual contact or indirect contact with objects like drinking fountains or telephones. Hepatitis B infections are difficult to treat and can be fatal. Prevention of hepatitis B is important. OSHA guidelines may require your employer to offer you immunizations against hepatitis B or provide follow-up care should you become exposed on the job.

HIV/AIDS

HIV, the human immunodeficiency virus, is the virus that causes AIDS (Acquired Immune Deficiency Syndrome). At this time, HIV infection and AIDS can be treated but cannot be cured. HIV infection usually leads to death once the infected person becomes weak and cannot fight off other infections. Many people infected with HIV may not feel or look sick. They may not even know that they have been infected. Only a blood test can detect HIV in the body. Because HIV infection is not curable, it is important to take steps to prevent HIV infection. Remember these facts:

1. HIV is **not** spread through casual contact.

2. The virus is easily killed by chlorine bleach, alcohol, and other common disinfectants. Washing carefully and using a disinfectant will kill the virus before it can enter your body.

3. HIV is transmitted only through exposure to infected blood, sexual intercourse, or breast milk.

Lifeguards should avoid direct and indirect contact with an injured person's body fluids. Contact with blood may allow the virus to enter your body through tiny breaks in the skin or other openings. Remember, there is no way for a lifeguard to know who may be infected with HIV or other communicable diseases. Because an injured person may not yet be ill and may not even know that he or she is infected, you must take the same basic precautions whenever you provide care.

Childhood diseases

Most people have been immunized against common childhood diseases, such as measles and mumps. Immunization is a way to help your own body prepare to fight an infection. Once immunized against a certain disease, it is less likely that you will contract the disease if that germ gets into your body. You may not have been immunized against all of the childhood diseases. If you are not sure which immunizations you have received or whether your immunizations are up to date, ask your doctor or health-care provider.

Protecting Yourself From Disease Transmission

The Exposure Control Plan

OSHA regulations require employers to have an Exposure Control Plan if an employee might be exposed to blood or other infectious substances as part of his or her job. Since your job as a lifeguard requires that you provide care to someone who is injured and who may be bleeding, this regulation often applies to you. The plan should specify guidelines to help prevent you from contracting any infectious diseases.

The Exposure Control Plan in your facility should be stored where you can read it. Become familiar with these guidelines. As the plan should explain specifically what you need to do at your facility to stay safe from infectious diseases.

Recommended Protective Equipment Against HIV and HBV Transmission

Task or Activity	Disposable Gloves	Gown	Mask	Protective Eyewear
Bleeding control with spurting blood	Yes	Yes	Yes	Yes
Bleeding control with minimal bleeding	Yes	No	No	No
Emergency childbirth	Yes	Yes	Yes, if splashing is likely	Yes, if splashing is likely
Oral/nasal suctioning manually clearing airway	Yes	No	No, unless splashing is likely	No, unless splashing is likely
Handling and cleaning contaminated equipment and clothing	Yes	No, unless soiling is likely	No	No

Excerpt from Department of Health and Human Services, Public Health Services: *A curriculum guide for public safety and emergency response workers prevention of transmission immunodeficiency virus and hepatitis B virus*, Atlanta, Georgia, February 1989, Dept. Health and Human Services, Centers for Disease Control.

Immunizations

Preventing infectious diseases begins with immunizations against these diseases:

- DPT (Diphtheria, pertussis, tetanus)
- Polio
- Hepatitis B
- MMR (measles, mumps, rubella)
- Influenza

Check with your doctor to see if your immunizations are up to date. OSHA requires that an employer make the hepatitis B vaccination available to all employees who may be exposed to blood or other body fluids. Therefore, as a lifeguard, you should have the hepatitis B vaccination. Your employer must provide this vaccination free and in a convenient way. Note that OSHA does not require the hepatitis B vaccination for all employees—just those likely to be exposed to blood or other body fluids when providing care. Other employees might receive a different kind of vaccination within 24 hours after exposure to blood or other body fluids. In all cases, be sure to immediately report any exposure to blood or body fluids to your facility manager or head lifeguard.

Precautions when providing care

Every time you provide care, follow universal precautions and safe practices, which include—

1. Personal hygiene
2. Personal protective equipment (basic precautions)
3. Work practices
4. Equipment cleaning and disinfecting

Lifeguards should use personal protective equipment (basic precautions) to prevent against disease transmission whenever providing care, regardless of the age or appearance of the victim. Remember, persons with some illnesses, such as HIV, may not show any signs or symptoms. An infected child or adult may not even know that he or she is infected.

Personal hygiene

Good personal hygiene habits, like frequent handwashing (Fig 13-5), help prevent disease transmission. You should always wash and scrub your hands after providing care, even if you never came into contact with blood or other body fluids.

Fig. 13-5

Personal protective equipment

Personal protective equipment (PPE)—also referred to as basic precautions—are all equipment and supplies that help keep you from directly contacting infected materials (Fig. 13-6). This includes disposable gloves (latex, vinyl, or nitrile) and resuscitation masks for giving rescue breathing. To avoid getting an infectious disease, follow these guidelines:

Fig. 13-6

- Wear disposable (single-use) gloves whenever giving care, particularly if you may contact blood or body fluids. This may happen directly through contact with a victim or indirectly through contact with soiled clothing or other personal articles.

- After providing care, remove your gloves by pinching the first glove at the wrist. Pull the glove toward your fingertips without completely removing it. With your partially gloved hand, pinch the exterior of the second glove at the wrist. Pull it toward your fingertips until it is inside out, and then remove it completely. Next grasp both gloves with your free hand, being careful to touch only the clean inner surface. Remove the gloves, and discard them in an appropriate container.

- Do not use gloves that are discolored, torn, or punctured.

- Do not clean or reuse disposable gloves.

- Avoid handling items, such as pens, combs, whistles, phones, or radios, when wearing soiled gloves.

- Keep any cuts, scrapes, or skin sores covered.

- Use breathing barriers, such as resuscitation masks.

Work practices

Work practices can help eliminate or reduce the risk of exposure at the facility.

Good work practices include—

- Place sharp items (e.g., needles, scalpel blades) in puncture-resistant, leakproof, labeled containers (Fig. 13-7).

Fig. 13-7

- Provide care that reduces splattering of blood or other infectious materials.

- Remove and dispose of soiled protective clothing as soon as possible.

- Clean and disinfect all equipment and work surfaces possibly soiled by blood or other body fluids.

- Wash your hands thoroughly with soap and water immediately after providing care. Use a utility or restroom sink, not one in a food preparation area.

- Do not eat, drink, smoke, apply cosmetics or lip balm, handle contact lenses, or touch your mouth, nose, or eyes when you are in an area where you may be exposed to infectious materials, such as a first aid room.

You should also know about any areas, equipment, or containers that may be contaminated. Biohazard warning labels are required on any container holding contaminated supplies, such as used bandages. Signs should be posted at entrances of work areas where infectious material may be present, such as a first aid room.

Equipment cleaning and disinfecting

After providing care always clean and disinfect the equipment that you use (Fig. 13-8). Handle all soiled equipment, supplies, or other materials with care until they are properly cleaned and disinfected. Place all used disposable items in labeled containers. Place all soiled clothing in marked plastic bags for disposal or washing (Fig. 13-9). To disinfect equipment soiled with blood or body fluids, wash it thoroughly with a mix of household chlorine bleach and water. The U.S. Centers for Disease Control and Prevention recommends a fresh mixture of about 1/4 cup of bleach per gallon of water. Floors, decks, and countertops must be cleaned of any soil you can see before using a bleach solution.

Fig. 13-8

Fig. 13-9

If you wear a uniform to work, wash and dry it according to the manufacturer's instructions. Scrub soiled boots, leather shoes, and other leather goods, such as belts, with soap, a brush, and hot water. In some situations you may have to clean an area soiled by blood or another body fluid. Wear disposable gloves and use paper towels to absorb the fluid, and dispose of these properly. Then cover the area with a mixture of bleach in water, and let that stand at least 20 minutes. Use more paper towels to absorb this disinfectant solution, and dispose of these properly.

If You are Exposed

If you are exposed to blood or another body fluid, wash the area as quickly as possible. Tell your supervisor and write down what happened. Some facilities may have special forms to document the exposure. Most facilities have a procedure to follow if you think you have been exposed to an infectious disease. Your supervisor or facility manager will make sure the right steps are taken. You may fill out a form to report what happened; see a doctor in some cases; or get a vaccination. Tests may also be done to see if you might need further treatment.

Putting it All Together

Some germs that enter the body can cause serious disease. When you provide care, you need to be careful to prevent those germs from infecting you. The biggest risks are from—

- Contacting a person's body fluids (direct contact).
- Touching a contaminated object (indirect contact).
- Breathing in air from an infected person.

The best way to prevent infection is to avoid contact with blood or other substances. Remember to follow universal precautions:

1. Personal hygiene

2. Personal protective equipment (basic precautions)

3. Work practices

4. Equipment cleaning and disinfecting

Use good personal hygiene practices, including frequent handwashing. When you provide care, use personal protective equipment. Wear disposable gloves and use a resuscitation mask whenever breathing for a victim. Wash your hands thoroughly after providing care, and properly dispose of any soiled materials or supplies. Use a mixture of bleach and water to clean equipment or soiled areas. Following the OSHA guidelines outlined in this chapter will greatly reduce your risk of contracting or transmitting an infectious disease when you provide care to an ill or injured person.

Appendix A

Health Precautions and Guidelines During Training

The American Red Cross has trained millions of people in first aid and CPR (cardiopulmonary resuscitation) using manikins as training aids. According to the Centers for Disease Control (CDC), there has never been a documented case of any disease caused by bacteria, a fungus, or a virus transmitted through the use of training aids such as manikins used for CPR.

The Red Cross follows widely accepted guidelines for cleaning and decontaminating training manikins. **If these guidelines are adhered to, the risk of any kind of disease transmission during training is extremely low.**

To help minimize the risk of disease transmission, you should follow some basic health precautions and guidelines while participating in training. You should take precautions if you have a condition that would increase your risk or other participants' risk of exposure to infections. Request a separate training manikin if you—

- Have an acute condition, such as a cold a sore throat, or cuts or sores on the hands or around your mouth.

- Know you are seropositive (have had a positive blood test) for hepatitis B surface antigen (HBsAg), indicating that you are currently infected with the hepatitis B virus.*

- Know you have a chronic infection indicated by long-term seropositivity (long-term positive blood tests) for the hepatitis B surface antigen (HBsAg)* or a positive blood test for anti-HIV (that is, a positive test for antibodies to HIV, the virus that causes many severe infections including AIDS).

- Have a type of condition that makes you unusually likely to get an infection.

If you decide you should have your own manikin, ask your instructor if he or she can provide one for you to use. You will not be asked to explain why in your request. The manikin will not be used by anyone else until it has been cleaned according to the recommended end-of-class decontamination procedures. Because the number of manikins available for class use is limited, the more advance notice you give, the more likely it is that you can be provided a separate manikin.

You can further protect yourself and other participants from infection during CPR training by following these guidelines:

- Wash your hands thoroughly before participating in class activities.

- Do not eat, drink, use tobacco products, or chew gum during class when manikins are used.

- Clean the manikin properly before use. For some manikins, this means vigorously wiping the manikin's face and the inside of its mouth with a clean gauze pad soaked with either a solution of liquid chlorine bleach and water (sodium hypochlorite and water) or rubbing alcohol. For other manikins, it means changing the rubber face. Your instructor will provide you with instructions for cleaning the type of manikin used in your class.

- Follow the guidelines provided by your instructor when practicing skills such as clearing a blocked airway with your finger.

> * *A person with hepatitis B infection will test positive for the hepatitis B surface antigen (HBsAg). Most persons infected with hepatitis B will get better within a period of time. However, some hepatitis B infections will become chronic and will linger for much longer. These persons will continue to test positive for HBsAg. Their decision to participate in CPR training should be guided by their physician.*

After a person has had an acute hepatitis B infection, he or she will no longer test positive for the surface antigen but will test positive for the hepatitis B antibody (anti-HBs). Persons who have been vaccinated for hepatitis B will also test positive for the hepatitis antibody. A positive test for the hepatitis B antibody (anti-HBs) should not be confused with a positive test for the hepatitis B surface antigen (HBsAg).

Physical Stress and Injury

Training in lifeguarding requires physical activity. If you have a medical condition or disability that will prevent you from taking part in the practice sessions, please let your instructor know. Certain rescue skills pose the possibility of physical stress or injury. Always follow your instructor's directions and take the following precautions when performing rescue skills:

- When performing skills that require you to lift, lift with your legs, not with your back.

- Some rescue skills require you to hold your breath during a rescue. If you run out of air during a simulated underwater rescue, return to the surface. During simulated rescues, you and your partner will use predetermined signals to advise each other of any problems.

- Whether you are acting as the victim or the rescuer, do not hyperventilate before submerging. Doing so could cause you to lose consciousness.

- If you are acting as a rescuer, be especially careful to support the victim's head when the victim is being removed from the water.

Appendix B

References

American Alliance for Health, Physical Education, Recreation and Dance. *Safety Aquatics.* Sports Safety Series, Monograph #5. American Alliance for Health, Physical Education, Recreation and Dance, 1977.

American Heart Association. *Guidelines 2000 for Cardio-pulmonary Resuscitation and Emergency Cardiovascular Care.* Supplement to *Circulation* 102 (2000).

The American National Red Cross. *Adapted Aquatics: Swimming for Persons With Physical or Mental Impairments.* Washington, D.C.: The American National Red Cross, 1977.

_____. *Basic Water Safety.* Washington, D.C.: The American National Red Cross, 1988.

_____. *Community First Aid and Safety.* Boston: StayWell, 1993.

_____. *CPR for the Professional Rescuer.* Boston: StayWell, 1993.

_____. *Emergency Water Safety.* Washington, D.C.: The American National Red Cross, 1988.

_____. *Lifeguarding.* Washington, D.C.: The American National Red Cross, 1990.

_____. *Lifeguarding Today.* Boston: StayWell, 1995.

_____. *Safety Training for Swim Coaches.* Boston: StayWell, 1988.

_____. *Swimming and Diving.* Boston: StayWell, 1992.

_____. *Emergency Response.* Boston: StayWell, 1997.

_____. *Preventing Disease Transmission.* Boston: StayWell, 1993.

_____. *Oxygen Administration.* Boston: StayWell, 1993.

_____. *Workplace Training: Standard First Aid.* Boston: StayWell, 1999.

_____. *Automated External Defibrillation.* Boston: StayWell, 1998.

Armbruster, D.A.; Allen, R.H.; and Billingsley, H.S. *Swimming and Diving.* 6th ed. St. Louis: The C.V. Mosby Company, 1973.

Association for the Advancement of Health Education. "Counting the Victims." HE-XTRA 18 (1993):8.

Baker, S.P.; O'Neill, B.; and Karpf, R.S. *The Injury Fact Book.* Lexington, Massachusetts: Lexington Books, D.C. Heath and Co., 1984.

Beringer, G.B., et al. "Submersion Accidents and Epilepsy." *American Journal of Diseases of Children* 137 (1983):604-605.

Bruess, C.E.; Richardson, G.E.; and Laing, S.J. *Decisions for Health.* Dubuque, Iowa: William C. Brown Publishers, 1989.

Brown, V.R. "Spa Associated Hazards—An Update and Summary." Washington, D.C.: U.S. Consumer Product Safety Commission, 1981.

Clayton, R.D., and Thomas, D.G. *Professional Aquatic Management.* 2nd ed. Champaign, Illinois: Human Kinetics, 1989.

Centers for Disease Control and Prevention. "Drownings at U.S. Army Corps of Engineers Recreation Facilities, 1986-1990." *Morbidity and Mortality Weekly Report* 41 (1992):331-333.

_____. "Drownings in a Private Lake—North Carolina, 1981-1990." *Morbidity and Mortality Weekly Report* 41 (1992):329-331.

_____. "Suction-Drain Injury in a Public Wading Pool—North Carolina, 1991." *Morbidity and Mortality Weekly Report* 41 (1992):333-335.

_____. *Suggested Health and Safety Guidelines for Recreational Water Slide Flumes.* Atlanta, Georgia: U.S. Department of Health and Human Services.

_____. *Swimming Pools—Safety and Disease Control Through Proper Design and Operation.* Atlanta, Georgia: United States Department of Health, Education, and Welfare, 1976.

Chow, J.M. "Make a Splash: Children's Pools Attract All Ages." *Aquatics International* (1993):27-32.

Committee on Trauma Research; Commission on Life Sciences; National Research Council; and the Institute of Medicine. *Injury in America.* Washington, D.C.: National Academy Press, 1985.

Consumer Guide with Chasnoff, I.J.; Ellis, J.W.; and Fainman, Z.S. *The New Illustrated Family Medical & Health Guide.* Lincolnwood, Illinois: Publications International, Ltd., 1988.

Cooper, K.H. *The Aerobics Program For Total Well-Being.* New York: Bantam Books, 1982.

Council for National Cooperation in Aquatics. *Lifeguard Training: Principles and Administration.* New York: Association Press, 1973.

Craig, A.B., Jr. "Underwater Swimming and Loss of Consciousness." *The Journal of the American Medical Association* 176 (1961):255-258.

Ebben, A. *Pool Lifeguarding.* Studley, Warwickshire, England: The Royal Life Saving Society UK, 1993.

_____. "Scanning, Supervising and Observing." *Lifeguard* 1 (1992):22-23.

Ellis, et al. *National Pool and Waterpark Lifeguard Training Manual.* Alexandria, Virginia: National Recreation and Park Association, 1993 and 1991.

Fife, D.; Scipio, S.; and Crane, G. "Fatal and Nonfatal Immersion Injuries Among New Jersey Residents." *American Journal of Preventive Medicine* 7 (1991):189-193.

Gabriel, J.L., editor. *U.S. Diving Safety Manual.* Indianapolis: U.S. Diving Publications, 1990.

Gabrielsen, M.A. "Diving Injuries: Prevention of the Most Catastrophic Sport Related Injuries." Presented to the Council for National Cooperation in Aquatics. Indianapolis, 1981.

_____. *Swimming Pools: A Guide to Their Planning, Design, and Operation.* Champaign, Illinois: Human Kinetics, 1987.

Getchell, B.; Pippin, R.; and Varnes, J. *Health.* Boston: Houghton Mifflin Co., 1989.

Hedberg, K., et al. "Drownings in Minnesota, 1980-85: A Population-Based Study." *American Journal of Public Health* 80 (1990):1071-1074.

Huint, R. *Lifeguarding in the Waterparks.* Montreal: Aqua-Lude, Inc., 1990.

Johnson, R.L. *YMCA Pool Operations Manual.* Champaign, Illinois: Human Kinetics, 1989.

Kowalsky, L., editor. *Pool-Spa Operators Handbook.* San Antonio, Texas: National Swimming Pool Foundation, 1990.

Lierman, T.L., editor. *Building a Healthy America: Conquering Disease and Disability.* New York: Mary Ann Liebert, Inc., Publishers, 1987.

Litovitz, T.L.; Schmitz, B.S.; and Holm, K.C. "1988 Annual Report of the American Association of Poison Control Centers National Data Collection System." *American Journal of Emergency Medicine* 7 (1989):496.

Livingston, S.; Pauli, L.L.; and Pruce, I. "Epilepsy and Drowning in Childhood." *British Medical Journal* 2 (1977):515-516.

Maglischo, E.W. *Swimming Even Faster.* Mountain View, California: Mayfield Publishing Company, 1993.

_____. *Swimming Faster.* Palo Alto, California: Mayfield Publishing Company, 1982.

Marion Laboratories. *Osteoporosis: Is It in Your Future?* Kansas City, Marion Laboratories, 1984.

Mitchell, J. T. "Stress: The History, Status and Future of Critical Incident Stress Debriefings." *JEMS: Journal of Emergency Medical Services* 13 (1988):47-52.

Mitchell, J. T. "Stress and the Emergency Reponder." JEMS: Journal of Emergency Medical Services 15 (1987):55-57.

Modell, J.H. "Drowning." *New England Journal of Medicine* 328 (1993):253-256.

YMCA. *On the Guard II.* Champaign, Illinois: Human Kinetics Publishers, Inc., 1997.

National Committee for Injury Prevention and Control. *Injury Prevention: Meeting the Challenge.* New York: Oxford University Press as a supplement to the *American Journal of Preventive Medicine,* Volume 5, Number 3, 1989.

National Safety Council. *Injury Facts, 1999 Edition.* Itasca, Illinois: National Safety Council, 1999.

National Safety Council and Thygerson, A.L., editors. *First Aid Essentials.* Boston: Jones and Bartlett Publishers, 1989.

National Spa and Pool Institute. *American National Standard for Public Swimming Pools.* Alexandria, Virginia: National Spa and Pool Institute, 1991.

New York State Department of Public Health. *Drownings at Regulated Bathing Facilities in New York State,* 1987-1990. Albany, NY: New York State Department of Health, 1990.

_____. *Lightning Safety Tips.* Albany, NY: New York State Department of Health, 1984.

Payne, W.A., and Hahn, D.B. *Understanding Your Health.* St. Louis: Mosby-Year Book, Inc., 1989.

O'Connor, J. "A U.S. Accidental Drowning Study, 1980-1984." Thesis, University of Oregon, 1986.

O'Donohoe, N.V. "What Should the Child With Epilepsy Be Allowed to Do?" *Archives of Disease in Childhood* 58 (1983):934-937.

Orlowski, J.P.; Rothner, A.D.; and Lueders, H. "Submersion Accidents in Children With Epilepsy." *American Journal of Diseases of Children* 136 (1982): 777-780.

Palm, J. *Alert: Aquatic Supervision in Action.* Toronto, Canada: The Royal Life Saving Society Canada, 1978.

Pearn, J. "Epilepsy and Drowning in Childhood." *British Medical Journal* 1 (1977):1510-1511.

Pearn, J.; Bart, R.; and Yamaoka, R. "Drowning Risks to Epileptic Children: A Study From Hawaii." *British Medical Journal* 2 (1978):1284-1285.

Pia, F. "Observations on the Drowning of Nonswimmers" *Journal of Physical Education* (July 1974): 164-167.

Pia, F. *On Drowning,* Water Safety Films, Inc. (1970).

Pia, F. "Reducing Swimming Related Drowning Fatalities" *Pennsylvania Recreation and Parks* (Spring 1991): 13-16.

Pia, F. "The RID Factor as a Cause of Drowning" *Parks and Recreation* (June 1984): 52-67.

Quan, L., and Gomez, A. "Swimming Pool Safety—An Effective Submersion Prevention Program." *Journal of Environmental Health* 52 (1990):344-346.

Rice, D.P.; MacKenzie, E.J.; et al. *Cost of Injury in the United States: a Report to Congress 1989.* San Francisco, California: Institute for Health and Aging, University of California, and Injury Prevention Center, The Johns Hopkins University, 1989.

Robertson, L.S. *Injury Epidemiology.* New York: Oxford University Press, 1992.

Royal Life Saving Society Canada. *Canadian Life Saving Manual.* Toronto, Canada: The Royal Life Saving Society Canada, 1973.

Spinal Cord Injury Information Network. Facts and Figures at a Glance–June, 2000. Available at: http://www.spinalcord.uab.edu. Accessed on November 22, 2000.

Strauss, R.H., editor. *Sports Medicine.* Philadelphia: W.B. Saunders Co., 1984.

Torney, J.A., and Clayton, R.D. *Aquatic Instruction, Coaching and Management.* Minneapolis: Burgess Publishing Co., 1970.

_____. *Aquatic Organization and Management.* Minneapolis, Minnesota: Burgess Publishing Co., 1981.

United States Lifesaving Association. *Lifesaving and Marine Safety.* Piscataway, New Jersey: New Century Publishers, Inc., 1981.

Wintemute, G.J., et al. "The Epidemiology of Drowning in Adulthood: Implications for Prevention." *American Journal of Preventive Medicine* 4 (1988):343-348.

World Waterpark Association. *Considerations for Operating Safety.* Lenexa, Kansas: World Waterpark Association, 1991.

_____. *The Aquatic Facility Operator Manual.* The National Recreation and Park Association, National Aquatic Section, 1992.

Notes

Notes

Notes

Notes

Notes

Notes

Notes

Notes

Notes